my heart's in

greenwich village

my

heart's in greenwich village

S E O N   M A N L E Y

Funk & Wagnalls
New York

For the best of Villagers,
SUSAN, JOEL and PAT, and
for PETE because those
were the days.

contents

my heart's in

greenwich village

i'll meet you
      in greenwich village

I stood there feeling the excitement. Even on the platform of the Seventh Avenue Subway at Christopher Street, there was an air of anticipation. Two girls stood leaning against the dirty steel columns, one of them idly drumming her fingers against her art portfolio. A young man in Levis admired himself in the window of the gum machine, and then with great deliberation put a penny in the slot. He unrolled the gum paper as though he were rolling a cigarette on the range, and then continued to stare into the mirror, testing the gum in his mouth.

"They all look like kids to me," said my sister, Gogo.

"So are we," I said defensively.

"So this is the Village," said Gogo.

"You haven't seen it yet. Come on, let's go out to the street."

"This is a filthy, dilapidated subway platform, just like every other filthy, dilapidated subway platform I've ever seen," said Gogo. "Maybe worse."

"Don't grouch," I said. "Look at the graffiti. You didn't see anything like that at college."

"I didn't study writing on the wall at college," Gogo retorted, but the walls caught her interest anyway—and the steps leading up to the street floor had a legend of their own. In red chalk someone had written:

ONE FALSE STEP AND YOU'RE IN
THE VILLAGE

Someone had answered that in blue chalk:

ONE FALSE STEP AND YOU'RE IN BROOKLYN

Echoing an old Greek chorus, red chalk replied:

THERE'S NO SUCH PLACE AS THE VILLAGE

While blue had printed carefully:

ONLY THE DEAD KNOW BROOKLYN
(WITH THANKS TO THAT OLD VILLAGER,
THOMAS WOLFE)

And the walls had even more masterful declarations:

GOOD-BY, MA, GOOD-BY, PA, I'M
GETTING OFF AT CHRISTOPHER STREET

15

Or:

HOW DO YOU KEEP THEM DOWN ON THE FARM
AFTER THEY'VE SEEN WEST FOURTH?

To which someone had added:

JUST OFFER THEM A BATH

And finally:

WHY? ONLY UPTOWN IS DIRTY.

"They're not the walls of the Metropolitan Museum," said
Gogo. "I suppose if we stood here long enough, someone
would write on our backs."

She cleared the last two steps in a single movement—and
we went out into the light, the midmorning Greenwich Village light.

First we looked at the street—or the streets. It was bewilder-
ing. The Sheridan Square subway steps have been discouraging
bewildered riders for generations. You come out of the subway
like Jonah from the mouth of the whale to be immediately
tossed in the oceanic traffic of the Village. The sea lanes go in
every direction—trucks lumber down Seventh Avenue, buses
across Christopher, taxis down Bleecker. You are for a moment glued to the cement—unsure of yourself in every way—
almost calling for rescue.

"Watch out," said Gogo, grabbing me. "We'll never live to

know the Village. We'll get killed trying to cross the street. Which way do we go, anyway?"

"I don't know," I said. "It looked different last time."

"Famous last words."

"There's a park." I pointed behind us.

"You call that a park?"

"Well, we can sit down and talk it over."

"I don't have anything to say," said Gogo, "other than we're nuts—regular walnut, cashew, pecan nuts. Who thought of this idea anyway?

"Don't tell me," she added. "I'll tell you—my sister the nut."

"Come on," I said, "if we run, we can make it." We dashed across the roadway separating the subway island from Sheridan Square Park. Even Gogo breathed more easily.

"Terra firma," said Gogo.

"You girls Italian?" said a fellow leaning against the railing.

"No," I said. "Why?"

"Thought you spoke it."

"You mean *terra firma?* That's not Italian," I began, but Gogo pushed me through the gate.

"That's Egyptian," she said. "We're a couple of Egyptians in disguise. That's my sister Cleopatra, but she can't speak to strangers—except in Egyptian."

The fellow muttered something and crossed the street.

"Well, here we are," I said.

17

"Where?" asked Gogo.

"Here in the Village."

"Oh, what do you suppose they call this park?"

"I'll ask that old lady," I said.

The old lady couldn't speak English, but her Italian was fluent. It didn't matter that I didn't understand her; she talked to me at length.

"What did she say?" Gogo wanted to know.

"She only speaks Egyptian," I said. "Go ask her yourself."

A man sat down next to us.

"You girls Egyptian, I heard you say."

"No," said Gogo, "we're a couple of Russians in disguise. That's my sister Anna Karenina, but she can't speak to strangers—except in Russian."

"I can speak Russian," said the fellow.

"Not her Russian. But seriously, we're not Russians. We're a couple of Scottish border collies—we don't speak to strangers. We just bite."

"Okay," he said. "Okay, don't bite my ear off."

"This park is filled with mashers," Gogo said.

"Mashers? I haven't heard that since our grandmother used to warn us against them."

"I know how to handle them," said Gogo.

"That's obvious," I said.

"What's not so obvious," Gogo snapped, "is why we're here."

I knew why. Greenwich Village had always fascinated me.

18

The Village! In the first place, every young writer had to live sometime in Greenwich Village. After that, Paris perhaps, but certainly Greenwich Village first. It didn't matter whether you would ever write a word, whether it was all just some dream—just the desire seemed to drive you down the streets of the Village. Hadn't they all been here before us? The good and the not-so-good, writing in attics, in basements, pounding typewriters and pounding the streets in an effort to find copy, to find publishers, to find the future.

I used to get out of the subway station in Sheridan Square and imagine how many people had walked up these same stairs before me, and how many would walk behind me with the same kind of dreams that I carried in a battered old portfolio. Or I would imagine the days before the subway when the great figures of American literature haunted the Village. I could see Walt Whitman, eternally walking, first down the Brooklyn streets, then on that trip he so enjoyed on the ferry that connected Brooklyn to Manhattan, and then again walking fiercely. I could picture in my mind his white hair blowing in the wind, a squashed black hat atop it, a cape of romance billowing out behind him, as he familiarized himself with every street in lower Manhattan until he arrived at the Village, where he would go to that wonderful rendezvous of writers and talkers—Pfaff's. There, around one glorious oak table sat some of the giants of the nineteenth century: along with Walt Whitman that strange supernatural writer, Fitz-James O'Brien, who wrote a couple of his stories about the Village;

and Stephen Crane. Earlier, Edgar Allan Poe, desolate and alone, fighting the fierce fury within his heart with all the words he could command, walked the Village streets. And O. Henry, over there on Seventeenth Street, picked up stories the way we picked up fall leaves.

There are stories everywhere in the Village, on every corner, in every house; there are dreams hanging out of windows, strung up like laundry on clotheslines in the sky.

You can hear the footsteps of those who were there before us: Louisa May Alcott, who wrote part of *Little Women* on MacDougal Street; Mark Twain, who lived on Twelfth Street; Edna St. Vincent Millay, burning her candle at both ends, traveling the Staten Island Ferry, going back and forth as we all would do, and finding young love and young words in the Village parks, on the streets, and beneath the ailanthus trees. And Eugene O'Neill, too, a thin question mark roaming the streets of the Village, its streets allowing him to dream back in time to his own childhood, giving him the freedom to express a new world in drama.

They were all young, as I used to imagine them, and that perhaps more than anything led not only me but every young person to the Village. Being young is not something that one should waste alone; it needs all the rest of youth around you to give it a sharp edge, because everyone knows that being young can cut sharply and deeply.

Instead of taking the blood from our best friend's finger and holding it to our own pinpricked finger so we would be blood sisters forever, we had moved on and now swore loyalty to a different kind of life—a life that our parents would not understand, a life filled with freedom, poetry, concern for other people; a life of feeling and, we hoped, a life of learning and of doing the right things. Youth loves people—the flower children, as they are called today, love people, but alas only with the queer, strange love of childhood. Our love was of a different kind, a kind of growing-up love that meant we wore shoes on the streets of the Village instead of going barefoot, that we tried to work and to learn our crafts, that we tried to be part of the society around us even if we allowed ourselves to choose only the society we wanted.

The Village! It meant having fun, glorious fun, the kind of wild abandonment of racing down the Village streets in the spring, singing in Washington Square Park, and holding hands with a date on lower Fifth Avenue and looking up—straight up at the glories of that street with all of Manhattan towering about you.

For some of the boys it meant that the Village was their introduction to New York itself, the city that would challenge them, where they would make their careers, where they would find themselves. Many of them came from places far away—from farms or the West Coast or the Southwest—and always New York had been a beacon, as it had been a beacon to people who wanted to be something, wanted to do something, wanted to feel the world with a little more intensity than other people and perhaps even leave a mark on that world. Sometimes it seemed impossible to do; it was a world of pavement —gritty, hard, even then dirty and dusty. But always there would come some glorious day, the sky so bright and blue, the buildings so sharply edged against it, that we felt almost as a group that our heart could break as we looked upon the whole fantastic reach of the Village which was now our home.

My sister and I had never been complete outsiders to Manhattan. We had known it since we were children. We had grown up in a Scottish-Irish colony in the upper Nineties. We knew all the romance of a city street, the strange conflict of cultures, the wonderful democracy, the absolute enchantment of October in New York. But we had never lived in the Village and now we were to do that.

Live! That was what the Village was supposed to allow you to do. *Live!* We were determined to do it.

sundays in the village

On Sundays that first fall I went hunting for the past.

I tried to find in that curious mixture of tenement, broken-down nineteenth-century wooden houses, tall apartment buildings, shops, alleyways, squares, secret streets, and secret gardens, the past of the Village itself.

I had felt instantly that I belonged there and that I must know all about it. As a child I used to walk up and down the cobblestones of Ninety-sixth Street from West End Avenue to the river. I imagined then that if I put my ear to the stones themselves, I might hear the clang of distant horses' hoofs, the sharp metal of their shoes ringing in the past of the street. I looked for that past now in the Village.

It was easy for me to find. In the early morning I would walk over to the Hudson River and stand on a wharf that jutted out precariously into the water. On both sides the tugs would be tied up for a day of rest, looking almost like great curled dogs resting beside the knees of the city. Above, a few towering buildings would smile down on them with that curious blankness of Sunday when the black eyes and faces of the office buildings look strangely asleep.

In those early hours no one haunted the wharf; later there would be families with children, young lovers, boys and girls in a sudden spurt of activity after Sunday school, but in the early morning there was nothing except the buildings, this wharf, and the Hudson that I stared down into.

As I looked down upon it, it was not all happiness by any means. Cigar butts, yesterday's newspaper with its World War II headline, an old carnation, a bobbing apple, a bottle half-sinking (did it or did it not contain some message from some faraway ship?)—all of these eddied and moved in front of me. I was at an age when I just wanted to see, observe, make no decisions. I wanted to let life carry me as this river carried the good and the bad, until I could come into some port.

On the spot I now stood, Indians had once stood, and I straightened my shoulders at the thought. I never could find out just what they were called; some said the Sappokanikee, others the Sappocanicon, but Gogo would sometimes catch me reading a huge tome about the Village and would explain simply to someone who had come into our apartment:

25

"Don't worry about Seon; she won't talk to you, she's reading about the Sapps."

Well, they weren't saps, they were as smart as we were to settle in this spot that seemed curiously right, and even in the early 1940's still wonderfully fresh. When the Indians stood here, there were woods behind them and rich soil for their corn. There was no soil now. If I rubbed my hands against the wharf itself, there were just splinters and a little crust of dirt.

Behind me, up what is now Christopher Street and turning down Bleecker, were Charles, Perry, and Tenth streets—once a great estate that had been the home of Captain Peter Warren, the squire of the Village. On the hard pavement of streets that had replaced the farm it was impossible to reconstruct the past. The green of what was once called the Green Village—our Greenwich Village—had long since disappeared, except for the stray ailanthus trees, or the tumbling window boxes that bravely, even in the fall, put out stunted green geraniums or, occasionally, a handful of ivy as precarious as city living itself.

No, it was down here by the Hudson that I could recapture the past, or, walking slowly in the early Sunday morning before the church congregations poured out onto that great game preserve of the Indians, now partially preserved for games of Village children in Washington Square. I could stand later in the old Royalton Hotel listening to the fountain, which I had been told still gave forth a fresh taste of the past from the Minetta Water Trout Stream.

By Sunday noon I would have wandered down to what was

once Richmond Hill, at a point at Charleston and Varick streets that jutted out from the end of MacDougal just a little north of Spring Street. Here there would be much activity in the late morning, the Catholic Church of St. Joseph pouring its members out onto the street. Here the Italian colony that had come to the Village hundreds of years ago still worshiped, gathered together under the handsome domes of the church, then dispersing down the long streets—some making their way to the Little Italy of Mulberry Street, others moving back up, scattered as they were now all around the Village.

This was *the* Church, the famous old church of the immigrant, and it seemed appropriate that near it stood the shadow of the ghost of Richmond Hill—what had once been the home of Aaron Burr. In the eighteenth century the ground had been high enough so that Aaron Burr and his daughter Theodosia, then only a teen-ager, had been able to look across the green fields to New Jersey far away.

Just a little south lay the Lispenard Salt Meadows, under what is now Canal Street, surrounding a large pond at the foot of Richmond Hill. At one time called Burr's Pond, teen-agers of the eighteenth century skated there each winter.

All I found that fall, except that the winter was coming, was that some of the sidewalks had been washed by shopkeepers (a few shops were open early in the morning, selling fresh soft rolls). They had taken buckets and flung water from them in abandonment, washing away the grime of New York, letting it trickle in tiny little rivers off the curb. As I would try to imag-

27

ine what life had been like among the trees and heavy shrub-
bery that once grew here and the sound of the birds that once
sang in the great oaks, I would sometimes be depressed by the
present and the future that seemed to press upon me from all
sides.

Sometimes we felt we had no right to the present, being
young and the world so torn by war. My pain would spill out
in long walks.

Gogo would say: "Leave her alone; she's probably just the
ghost of Theodosia."

It was true that I was haunted by the figure of Theodosia
Burr—part child, part hostess, part daughter, part companion
to her father.

I could see them entertaining Talleyrand and Louis Philippe,
even Alexander Hamilton, who later would be mortally
wounded by Burr in Weehawken. I could see Theodosia entertaining the great Mohawk chief, Joseph Brant, and I suffered
her doubts that she could handle such a dinner party for an
Indian she supposed was a cannibal. Or I could see her later,
miserably drowned, as she undoubtedly was, on her way
back from Savannah when she was still a beautiful young girl.
Her ghost did indeed haunt me as I walked the streets of the
Village, hunting I do not know what, but finding more than I
could ever absorb.

They said her ghost used to walk up and down the shores of
Cape Hatteras, but for me her ghost haunted the Village. She

was as alive to me as the girl on the corner, a radiant girl emerging from the subway.

And then I would have a sudden change of mood; out of the past into the present and into the future. You cannot walk the streets of the Village without meeting friends. They greet you from shops and churches, from stoops, from the windows of upper stories; and there were many basement apartments, so you were shouted at from the bowels of the earth, too. There were friends in Washington Square, friends on the even then convivial MacDougal Street, friends down Christopher, West Fourth, West Eighth, friends standing in the Sunday sunshine on Fifth Avenue, friends later in the day along the wharfs, friends on the Christopher Street Ferry. Regularly by late afternoon on Sundays we would pile onto the old ferry and make our way to Weehawken. After a day of dreaming of Theodosia Burr, it seemed to be an apt ending.

Gogo and my friends were used to my moodiness, used to my coming to terms with the Village and myself, and as we would settle back in one of the clam houses in Weehawken, someone was always bound to say:

"The ghost of Theodosia Burr always disappears for Seon in a dozen clams on the half shell."

We all ate lustily. After all, weren't we Villagers, and wasn't the Village for those who wanted to taste life with all the freshness of a Bleecker Street apple, with all the sharpness of a clam on the half shell?

29

village rain
    for the complexion

When you first come to the Village as a girl, you are not as independent as you think. So it wasn't unusual that our first apartment should be shared with a group of roommates, new faces coming and going, new eccentricities to be learned, new laws to be put up in the bathroom. *Never, Never Touch My Cold Cream* said one large sign, which Peggy had initialed. Underneath she had put in parentheses, "It's part of my career, you know."

The rest of us all had our cold cream touched, or our lipstick appropriated. Our comb disappeared, our toothpaste was left uncapped, our toothbrush was lost or had been used to clean a comb. None of us had managed to think up any trenchant statement that the toothbrush and the comb were necessary for our careers, so we regarded Peggy's career with fascination.

Peggy was our actress. Not only that, Peggy had actually discovered this apartment, one of the most attractive in the Village, but perhaps one that the original owners did not think would be now sheltering six girls—six girls with very diverse habits, dreams, and, as Mary Anne muttered, "careers." Mary Anne wouldn't have a thing to do with that actress business. She was going to be a painter, and we could follow her career in the bathroom by the pigments of blue, burnt umber, sage green, crimson—the remains of which always scarred the bathroom sink.

It was not surprising in the morning to hear Peggy wailing like some Irish banshee because Mary Anne had worked late the night before on a particularly vivid canvas and had dripped some red paint on Peggy's freshly ironed blouse.

"Oh, shut up, Peggy. Now you can play Lady Macbeth," said Ernestine, our great singer.

We had a great actress, a great painter, a great musician— Ernestine, of course, who day and night practiced in the tiny room off the hallway.

"I think she's trying to break the chandelier," Gogo would moan.

"No," said Peggy, "just our eardrums."

"No," said Mary Anne, "just our nerves. After all, it is wartime. Perhaps she's a spy."

It was wartime and the Village had a curious look of womanhood about it, or more particularly, of girlhood. It was like the kind of villages I was to see later in Europe—some villages

33

without any young people, other villages without any adults, some without any middle-aged people.

The Village had always been a little in exile from the rest of Manhattan, and the young people who went there immediately after college were a little in exile from the outside world. The Village is a transition place—a place between the wilds of adolescence and the more steadied maturity that is to come. Some people, however, know the wonder, the dedication that imbues the Village, so they stay there, or they are called back to the Village by some term or phrase in the newspaper, by some remembered smell of chestnuts in the air, or by recalling the scent of the first fire in the fireplace in one's very first apartment.

Peggy was against using our fireplace. It dried out her skin. An actress had to have a good complexion—soft and delicate.

Gogo would say to me, "An actress must have the disposition of a toad; that is, if this is a good example."

"No," said Mary Anne, "the disposition of a wildcat."

Our singer said nothing. She would just sing some arias, more fiercely than ever, and Peggy would turn white.

"You know I've got a rehearsal tomorrow, Ernestine, you know I do. My nerves can't take that kind of sound. And what's this, Seon? Don't tell me this is canned spaghetti for dinner. You know my figure can't take that."

"Our budget can't take anything else." I felt belligerent.

"Why don't you do something decent?" Peggy said. "Something that contributes to society. And maybe you could make some money instead of working in that stupid bookshop."

"I like it," I said. "I could get you a job there."

"I have to watch out for my feet," said Peggy. "An actress's feet are important, and . . ."

"My feet are important too," interrupted Gogo, who was working in a shop, "but I would risk the chance of hurting them just for one good solid kick on—"

"No," I said, "she would just suffer for her art, you know."

Our apartment looked out onto the small slate roof of another house behind us, snuggling up like mother and child as so many Village houses do. We didn't dare go out on the roof, but it was a meeting place for every cat in the vicinity. The Village cats were as omnipresent as the cats of Venice. We named them all. There were Discovery and Devil, Rudyard Kipling, A. Conan Doyle, and there was a beautiful female tabby called Jane Austen. Then there was an entire rival group of cats that came barreling over the roof, who knows from where, just to sit and stare at us in the morning as we all got dressed. It must have been a fascinating spectacle, even to cats, because eccentricities jostled hairbrushes and combs, and tempers were short.

We ourselves used to watch Peggy each morning because she had arranged out on the back roof a collection of those wonderful old stone jars that Dundee Marmalade used to come in.

"What are they for?" asked Gogo.

"I'm collecting rainwater," said Peggy. "It's good for my complexion."

We never told her that we all used to see the cats lapping up her water in the course of the day.

"A little cat tongue won't hurt her any," said Gogo.

"It might make her cattier," said Ernestine.

"And just suppose she does grow a little fur around her face. She could always play in *Puss and Boots*."

Our Village had then, and still has, the feeling of a small town. We immediately made friends with the Chinese laundryman, who called us nice ladies.

"Here come the nice ladies," he would say to his little boy, and would stand up a bit straighter. (He took extra time over Peggy's blouses, because too much starch might irritate her neck and her neck, of course, was important to her career.)

"Particularly if she wanted to play a swan," said Gogo.

The florists of the Village were my first and continued delight. There is something about fall in the Village that is less poignant than fall in the country. Part of it is the leaves, of course. They are all somewhat artificial. They will not fall from their branches. They are brighter and more vivid than nature itself. I could stand outside of the florist shop and look in to the countryside within. Or I could put my hands on the leaves that stood in the pots outside. The sweet eucalyptus mixed with the colorful fall leaves, all treated and waxed so that they could bear the heat (if you had heat) of the Village apartments. Then there was the bittersweet, the pods bursting with color, or the dried herbs that looked like mummified country weeds.

Sometimes a lone red flower would come for Peggy from the corner florist, the card simply saying "An Admirer." We used to speculate as to who sent it. One of the local actors living in the Village?

Ernestine would stop singing long enough to say, "Don't be silly. I think she has them sent here herself."

Actually this living together, roommates in the Village, was just an extension of college. We were all trying out our new independence. There was no curfew; we had no housemother. Our dates would drop us home, in all honesty, earlier than they had at college, because they all had to get up early for their jobs—jobs they disliked, temporary jobs until they would go into the Army. All our dates were fascinated with Peggy. She would greet them regally at the door, holding out her hand, a princess among commoners.

"Is she really an actress?" Ted would ask, or Bob, or John.

"She certainly acts for us," Gogo told them.

"She's got a walk-on," I said, defending anyone willing to take the risk of the arts.

"I can't imagine anyone letting her walk on," said Gogo. "The tough thing to do is to get Peggy to walk off. Once she's on the stage she has a stance like a bulldog. You have to push her off."

"What's the walk-on?"

"I think it's in that new production of *Alice in Wonderland*," I said. "I think she's one of the flowers."

"Skunk cabbage," muttered Ernestine.

"You girls are jealous," the boys would say.

"Yes," I said. "We are. At least she's got her career under way."

"I lost my job," said Ted.

"I thought so," I said. "I could tell when you came in."

"Could you get me a job at the bookshop?"

"I think so."

The bookshop I worked in uptown was large and cavernous. There always seemed to be room for one more.

"Would you mind working in the basement store?" I asked.

"Oh," said Ted. "Does it have less prestige?"

"Yes," I admitted. "The basement isn't quite as important as the first floor."

"What's in the basement?"

"Oh, Bibles and things like that," I said. "Don't worry about it. It's fun. Gypsy Rose Lee was down there just the other day."

"What was she doing? Inscribing the Bible?" said Ted.

"Stupid—just autographing her new book."

"Doesn't that strike you as strange? Don't they generally have autograph parties on the first floor?"

"Yes," I said.

"Poor Gypsy Rose," Ted said. "Sending her off to the basement like that. Was she wearing clothes?"

"Of course she was wearing clothes."

The conversation had interested Peggy, of course.

"I didn't know you got actresses there," she said.

"There are lots of actresses," I said. "The assistant manager is an old drama critic."

"Well, what about that," said Peggy. "Do you think you could get me a job there?"

"Well, they don't put up with much nonsense. You've really got to work. You just can't go posing behind revolving doors."

"Who do you have besides Gypsy Rose Lee?"

"Oh, Margaret Sullavan was in, and Jean Arthur—lots of actresses."

"And actors too?" said Peggy.

"Of course," I said.

"Maybe I'll think about working there after all," said Peggy.

"Thanks, we need you."

I wasn't impressed by the actors and actresses who came in, but occasionally I would be haunted by the face and figure of somebody I had known only in words, but whom I knew so much better. One day Willa Cather came in in her long fur coat, the one that circled her ankles as though she were being embraced by some Scandinavian bear. I had been so impressed that my hand shook as I wrapped her package. I wanted to tell her that she was a great writer, that I was delighted to see her, that I had read all her books, but all I had been able to manage was "Thank you, Miss Cather." And T. S. Eliot coming in for one of his own books of poetry to send to somebody. "Just from England, you know," he said. "I brought no copies." I wrapped his package with particular care.

Or e. e. cummings, the cummings I knew from the Village, and it was strange to see him in an uptown shop. It was often strange to see the world of the Village make its way uptown. But even in those first months of roommates and our first fall in New York, one could tell that few of us would last. Peggy was bound to go up to midtown to one of the theatrical rooming houses which would give her the kind of excitement she wanted. Mary Anne would have a studio. Ernestine would have a small apartment near Carnegie Hall. But Gogo and I by that time were true Villagers—we would not leave.

a room with a fireplace

Your first apartment in the Village should have these four essentials:

1) a fireplace, even if it doesn't work—or even if you can't afford wood for one that does work;
2) wisteria on the outside of the house, even if there is no paint on the inside;
3) rickety, romantic stairs—the higher they go the better;
4) French windows that let the crooked afternoon Village light come streaking across the floor, and that also let the snow pile up on the floor, the rain beat across your only piece of upholstered furniture.

Gogo and I, having found that all those roommates were just too much, decided to get an apartment of our own. We looked for all four of the above-mentioned essentials, but *we*

42

had a fifth requirement that most girls did not need—a cellar for our printing press. We also acquired a bonus in our first apartment together—a beguiling, adventuresome rat called Joey.

The printing press wasn't large, but we had expended upon it a sizable inheritance and it stood there glaring at us from the basement in which we placed it temporarily. Glaring at us because you cannot place a printing press temporarily. It wants to be in the center of things, the center of a room in which a lot of copy is being set up in those intricate little brass patterns that mean the words have been printed for posterity.

Our press began to appear to us as an ungainly, impossible, imbecilic pet. Actually, if you stare down at a printing press from any height, it looks unusually stupid. It can't move, or doesn't care to move, unless you choose to move it. How could such a non-speaking, almost faceless machine stupidly control our lives, even dictate where we would live?

"It shouldn't be hard," said Gogo.

"Hard what?" I said. All life seemed terribly hard that morning.

"It shouldn't be hard to get a fireplace and wisteria."

"It shouldn't be hard," I said, "to find French windows and a place for the printing press. After all, the Village has had loads of little printing presses. There must be plenty of land-ladies who'd like to take in two girls and a printing press."

And then as I said the words aloud, I realized that it didn't seem too favorable. Two girls and a printing press certainly didn't seem to be suitable uptown. Why did we suddenly decide it would be suitable in the Village?

Each time we moved the press, it was a devastating financial experience. We were both working now. I worked in another bookshop, endlessly torn by my desire to read every book in the shop. Gogo was working for a photographer, hoping that eventually she'd be as great as Berenice Abbott, who had photographed all of the superb writers and artists of the twenties from James Joyce to the painter Man Ray and who lived right around the corner from us. We passed her each morning now, as we walked to the corner for coffee in Riker's and a look at the great new exciting world of Greenwich Village.

On our days off, if they coincided, we could sit there in Riker's window together and look leisurely at a Village morning.

It was superb. Everybody got up late, or so it seemed. The ant life of early morning activity, with everybody rushing madly to make a nine o'clock day, had disappeared and instead, along about ten-thirty each morning, the Village came to with a new kind of life. It was a life of slower measure, a life not of blind rush but of quiet, determined dedication.

The Villagers who came out of the doors at ten-thirty seemed to be still stretching their spiritual arms and heartstrings as they stood on the corners of their streets before walking down Seventh Avenue to pick up the morning paper. After picking up the paper, they would go on to Riker's or the drug-

a room with a fireplace

store and have a cup of coffee that, unlike coffee in suburban homes or the homes we had come from, disassociated you with your home and associated you, instead, with the outside world. We were part of that world now. We were Village.

In the Village much can happen to you while you are having your cup of coffee. We could almost mark some of the great times of our life, our great discoveries, by random cups of coffee. So it was in October, a beautiful October day (all of New York is beautiful or can be or used to be, in October). What they once called the champagne air of the twenties hadn't been quite dissipated in the early forties.

Beyond the little confines of the Village there was still a war going on, but if you did not immediately read the front page of the newspaper, and simply looked out on the street itself with that wonderful blue light and all of the buildings sharp and somewhat more clear than they are even in reality, the Village was the place to live.

And those who sat next to you on the precarious stools of Riker's coffee shop seemed monumental. Some of them were, of course. They did not seem to fit comfortably on the stools, and arms would dig you in the ribs, packages would fall across the morning paper, occasional cups of coffee would be spilled.

We sat down one morning next to Jeffrey Bone. Jeffrey Bone was not bigger than life size. He was just as his name implied—long, British, bony, and between ships in the Merchant Marine. We had met him, as you met everybody sooner

45

or later in the Village—more close-knit than the proverbial country village—we had met him having coffee at another cafeteria with friends the week before. That was more than just an introduction. There was no formality in our formations of friendship. Most people knew they would be in the Village probably only for a short time, the men and boys even less because of the war still going on.

Now Jeffrey Bone sat beside us in Riker's, with that look on his face, a look I had become very familiar with in the Village. It implied "I'd like to treat you girls—but the truth is could you pay for my coffee?" He drank half his coffee—another ploy we had discovered that was used with great frequency, because nobody took half a cup of coffee away from somebody who was unable to pay. He wiped his mouth carefully with a paper napkin as though it was the finest damask, and said, in the expected fashion, "Girls, can you pay for my coffee today?"

"Oh, Jeffrey," said Gogo.

"We'll pay," I said, because I could see Jeffrey had something on his mind. Occasionally, he had something interesting to say. Not too much, but he had come from the Wordsworth country of England and I clothed him with a somewhat romantic eighteenth-century air in which, this morning, for example, he should not have been sitting here in Riker's at all but should have been striding the hills and dales of Westmoreland.

I knew I would hear from Gogo later. She said I always was

46

a sucker. "If some guy looked like Keats, God knows what you'd do," she said. Well, Jeffrey didn't look like Keats. He didn't look like Wordsworth. He didn't look like Kipling. He just looked like himself, and that almost wasn't worth a coffee, but I'd pay it anyway.

"Do you two want an apartment of your own?" he said.

There, I thought to myself, Gogo doesn't have enough faith in human beings. One cup of coffee and we hear about an apartment. That's the way to do it. If we went to one of those agencies, we'd have to pay an extra month's rent.

"What kind of an apartment?" said Gogo, cautiously.

"Oh, one just right for you girls."

"Does it have a fireplace?" I asked.

"It's got a great fireplace," said Jeffrey. "Of course," he continued only a little apologetically, "of course, you can't use it. You can't burn anything in it—you'd burn the house down. But you could put flowers in it."

"Fireweed, I suppose," said Gogo nastily, "or firecrackers. We could sit around in the winter toasting firecrackers."

I ignored her.

"Does it have wisteria, Jeffrey?"

"I guess so. You can't tell in October, but it's got some kind of vine all over the front."

"Probably pulling the house up by its roots," muttered Gogo.

"What about French windows?"

"It *does* have French windows," said Jeffrey. "Of course,

some of the windows don't have any windowpanes, but that isn't so bad."

"Oh, not at all," said Gogo sweetly, "now that winter's coming, what could be nicer? We can ski in the living room."

"Does it have rickety, rackety stairs?" I asked.

"What do you expect, an elevator?" said Jeffrey. "You girls certainly look a gift apartment in the mouth. Of course it has stairs. Five glorious flights of them straight up to the sky."

"Does it have room for the printing press?" I said.

Now, everybody in the Village knew about our printing press. It was like carrying around an unhousebroken pet that we were having trouble finding a home for. A home with us, of course. We did not want it far separated from us.

Jeffrey hesitated a moment.

"Well, I'm not sure. You know, all these old floors in the Village are pretty scandalous. My last bookcase went through my floor."

"I think we ought to get rid of the press," said Gogo.

"Where's the apartment?" I asked quickly.

"On Barrow Street," said Jeffrey. "All the good apartments are on Barrow Street."

It was a good name, I thought, and a good indication, too, because my idle study of the Village had told me that Barrow Street used to be Reason Street, that Tom Paine had lived there at one point, and that his house around the corner on Bleecker Street was rumored to be still standing—amidst a little group of dilapidated wooden houses.

As I set down my cup of coffee, I knew Barrow Street was the right place. I could see myself as the female Tom Paine, turning out on our dear press superb calls to justice. Who knew, perhaps with Robert or with Wayne we might write another *Age of Reason*. We might inspire the troops; we might change the pattern of the world. And as I brooded about all these possibilities, Gogo drew herself up and said with great practicality, "How much does it cost?"

The apartment could be had for thirty-eight dollars. It had one room, or as Jeffrey described it, one beautiful room, looking down on a garden; one bedroom that was not so beautiful; a usable kitchen unit; and a bathroom. For those days, this was a bourgeois paradise and the truth was that the description sounded comfortable enough.

"What about the press?" I said.

"That's your concern, Seon," said Jeffrey rather bitterly. "Can't you be separated from that stupid press? Leave the press where it is, and begin to *live!*"

Jeffrey had been such a superb salesman that we bought him another cup of coffee, and then we walked slowly to the residence he had described. It had now taken on a gorgeous brilliance, in our mind's eye, under the October sun. When we got outside, it still looked pretty good. Of course, there was no paint on the house, but I did see an indication of a wisteria vine. I had always been a sucker for wisteria. And in the spring, the vines would certainly climb up to cover the paintless front.

49

We rang the doorbell.

The door was opened, not by a landlady the way I imagined it might be—a large, somewhat motherly woman—but by a cranky old man. As he stood there petulantly looking out at us, I caught a glimpse from the side of my eye of a household pet, a cat, I felt. But it wasn't a cat at all—an enormous rat ran out of the door.

So we were introduced to Joey, our rat. It was not, I felt, an auspicious beginning. Gogo said nothing; she was far too startled. Jeffrey was going into a rather long and involved explanation of why the old man should give him a tip for having located such ideal tenants. And I was gathering my forces to approach the matter head-on.

"I didn't think there'd be rats," I said.

The old man looked me up and down. I was a poor example of young Village womanhood.

"Where you have rats," he said simply, "you don't have mice."

This seemed to be a convincing argument. Mice didn't bother Gogo and me, but they might bother some of our girl friends, so we were protecting them from that awful fate. I went up the stairs still muttering, "I don't like rats," and I could hear strange, furtive sounds in the little garbage pails that were placed in front of the doors. Joey's friends, I guessed.

"You'd be lucky to get it," said Jeffrey.

"Got your security?" said the old man.

Security was an important word to us. If you had the thirty-eight dollars for the rent, you still needed another thirty-eight dollars for security. What security? I often wondered. The security of having your own private rat in your own private Village apartment. As I looked up the long, black stairs, I could see a glimmer of light coming from the top. Somehow or other it was magical; even a Village light coming through a crooked window was perfect. I felt a curious sense of being at home, even before I opened the door.

But I didn't open the door. The old man kicked it. The door gave way reluctantly, so reluctantly that he had to kick it again, and one hinge became so loosened that the door had to be lifted up and carried inward bodily before it would open. It was a strange, unhappy door, and it stayed that way until we left, because already being such a superb apartment, no further "improvements" were to be made.

The apartment looked down, as Jeffrey had said, upon a garden. It was, as all the Village gardens were, a cement garden struggling madly against the approaching winter. The ailanthus tree was tall and miserable. The house next door was double in size and shielded the garden from any light or even air. On the right-hand side, however, there was a garden restaurant. We could see, sitting at one of the tables that October morning, an old Italian gentleman, still in his shirtsleeves, smoking one of those fabulous twisted black cigars that were sold so commonly in the Village. Beside him there was an enormous cat, in front of him a bottle of wine, and above him a leaf from an ailanthus tree straggled down.

We were young, healthy, and with our noses pressed up against the broken French window—an incredibly grimy cracked window—we could see that this was a new world for us. We had our first apartment in the Village.

We moved in. Our furniture was Early Methodist. It had come from the church sales at the Methodist Church, and because we were now entering into a real bohemian period, we knew the terribly bourgeois darkness of it must be eliminated. We spent that weekend painting.

Even today the glory of a fall in New York is accompanied by young people gathered into little groups in the paint stores of the Village, changing their whole way of life with a couple of quarts of Benjamin Moore paint and some brushes.

We succeeded superbly. We had paid the great abstract painter Hans Hofmann a visit, and he and his wife Maria had brought from their house on the Cape some of their magnificent tomato-red chairs. With one of those terrible streaks of genius that comes over you when aided and abetted by another, be it sister, cousin, friend, or even later, husband or wife, we painted the entire apartment furniture, in honor of Hans and Maria Hofmann, tomato red.

Jeffrey visited us the evening after we finished. He could see none too clearly, for we had only a small light bulb hanging in the center of the room. But he studied the effect and moaned gently, "It's going to be like living in a ketchup factory. And look at yourselves!"

I looked at Gogo. Either she was hemorrhaging badly or she was a worse painter than I was. We had only the one electric bulb—the paint and the "security" non-security had taken all our funds. So to look at ourselves in the bathroom, we had to stand up on the already painted red table in the living room, unscrew the bulb, hot and terrible to the hand, and reinsert it in the bathroom socket. We looked then in the mirror, and life seemed a complete defeat.

"Don't worry," Jeffrey said kindly. "It'll come off."

"How?" I said.

"Scrubbing," he said. "That's the only way to do it."

So we scrubbed. We scrubbed for days, it seemed, before the red eventually came off. But at the bookshop, I hovered in the back of the tremendously dark and dirty store. I still had some red-enameled hair and it stood out rather like that of the Bride of Frankenstein.

The lady above us used to say that she knew we were nice girls, we had such a well-scrubbed look that first year. We didn't have the heart to tell her why. The following spring we found Joey still pushing paint cans down those long, rickety steps. We thought he stopped just long enough to sniff the sweet wisteria. Even Joey was *living*.

the time we got
the plague—almost

The daylight grew increasingly shorter and even on the weekends it seemed as though we would never see the sunlight, no matter how hard we twisted our necks and pushed our faces against the dirty windows.

"You and your fantasies about the Arctic," said Gogo.

"It isn't the Arctic. It's more like the black hole of Calcutta. Well, you and your fantasies about Robert Clive," I said, and then we both huddled in our chairs for a moment.

"We can't go on like this," said Gogo. "We'll never see daylight again. We'll go out into the sunlight and our eyes will be just slits. No one will look at us. Our skin will get the worst kind of pallor."

"Oh, shut up," I said. "Gogo, you're too dramatic."

"Not as dramatic as you are," she said.

"We could die here," I moaned. "Everybody's away this weekend and we could die here, far from the sun."

"I wouldn't die here," said Gogo. "I have too much dignity to die in this hole of an apartment. Come on, Seon, let's look for another apartment. Nothing could be worse than this."

"I don't feel too well," I said. "I think I'm coming down with something."

"Brain fever," said Gogo. "You're working around too many books."

"You used to say that," I said, "when we were children. I loathed you for it."

"Well, wasn't it true?" she said. "Who would have found this apartment but someone suffering from a severe case of brain fever, or snow blindness, or—"

"Oh, shut up," I said.

"What do you think you're getting?" she asked sympathetically.

"Gogo, I have an awful headache, and I feel hot, and you wouldn't believe it, but I think I'm getting the measles."

"Measles?" she said. "How could you be getting measles?"

"There were measles in the bookshop."

"What do you mean? Walking-around measles?"

"Mrs. Johnson had the measles," I said.

"That's funny," she said, "Mr. Walters in the photography shop had the chicken pox."

"Oh, no," I moaned.

"Do you feel worse?" she asked.

"No, I was just thinking. Suppose you come down with the chicken pox, and I've got the measles, and we're all alone here in this—"

"In this tomb, that's what it is," Gogo said. "It's a regular Edgar Allan Poe tomb. If you dug at those walls, the bodies of everybody who was ever miserable in the Village would come tumbling out, nothing but skeletons."

"I'm burning up," I said.

"Go to bed," said Gogo sweetly. "Go to bed and put the rug over you. It's not a blanket you need, but a nice rug. I never feel better than when I'm sleeping under that rug."

I couldn't argue with her. I had never known anybody in my life who slept under a rug, but if Gogo wanted to have that idiosyncrasy, it was a darn sight better than many you could find in the Village.

"Shall I make you some spaghetti?" she said.

"No," I moaned.

"Shall I go out and get you a slice of pizza?"

"Oh, no," I said.

"Clam chowder?"

"No!"

That exhausted her immediate culinary repertoire, and she fell silent.

"You could die in New York and nobody would care," she said.

"That's what they always say," I muttered. "Gogo, maybe

I'll take that rug after all, but put it on me gently. I feel as though my bones are falling apart."

"Maybe you got something from Joey," she suggested. "The plague, perhaps. We live so close to the water that maybe Joey really escaped from a plague ship."

"Gogo," I said bitterly, "you need something for your mind really to explore. Your imagination is just too rich."

"Well, it may be richer than yours," she said. "Certainly, we could do a lot better than having $1.50 between us on a winter's afternoon, all alone in the city, maybe dying."

"I'm not dying," I said, "but I am feeling miserable."

She was quiet for a few minutes, or so it seemed. I don't know how long it was because I had fallen asleep under her rug. The rug turned out to be very comfortable, rough on the inside, kind of smooth and prickly on the outside. If you picked at it, you got little bits of grass out of it, I thought, but it was probably just the debris that country feet had carried over the rug. I didn't know why we had ever moved from the country. We liked the country. The country was beautiful and green, and even in the winter you could look out and see a fine horizon. Everybody needed a horizon. There wasn't any horizon in this room, or maybe there was, for as my fever got worse, the horizon began to tilt and turn. I felt hot and uncomfortable. I kicked off the rug, not an easy thing to do. It weighed a tremendous amount.

"That's the only rug we have left of Mama's," said Gogo.

"I've always liked that rug. Remember, we used to have it in the library."

"I remember it," I said.

We were shy about discussing the past together. It seemed so long ago and far away, and so much had happened since. Our life had fallen into so many different periods: our childhood in New York, then a completely different adolescence in Connecticut, then college sharply separating both, and now this life—today at least—desperately alone in New York.

"Of course, we're not alone," said Gogo. "We've got loads of friends."

"What kind of friends are they?" I said.

"Well," she started ticking them off, "there's Jeff, there's Max, and there's Costa, and there's Manuel. There's Mary Anne and—"

"Oh," I interrupted, "yes, they're friends, but we ought to have a doctor who's a friend. Somebody who knows something about measles, or something like that. I think we ought to get a doctor, Gogo. I really feel terrible."

"Well, I don't want to frighten you, Seon," said Gogo, "but I feel terrible too. Move over. I'm going to get into the bed."

We must have dozed for the rest of the afternoon. When I woke up, it appeared to be night. One never knew; it was always so dark in the apartment. I had nothing over me, and Gogo was wrapped up in the rug. I was tempted to unroll her sharply and sprawl her out on the floor, but I looked at her and noticed she had spots—spots all over her face.

"Gogo," I screamed, "you've got spots."

"Go to sleep," she said, "go to sleep."

I repeated, "Gogo, you've got spots."

I put on our one little bedroom light, and she opened her eyes cautiously.

"I've got spots? Well, look at you; you've got spots. What does it matter? We both have spots."

"We can't change our spots probably," I said. "You're delirious, Gogo. You've got spots and I've got spots—we've both got the measles."

"Or we both have chicken pox," said Gogo, struggling up on her elbows. "Oh, how horrible to die here alone from chicken pox, far away from everybody in this black hole of Calcutta. I kept telling you to make more money and put in a telephone."

"Everybody we know stops by," I said. "Sometimes you can't stop people from stopping by. Seems to me hundreds of people stop by here each and every day. I get so tired of their stopping by."

"Well, nobody stopped by today," warned Gogo. "Nobody stopped by, and we'll probably get sicker and we'll get a terrible thirst. That's what happened in the plague."

"It's not the plague," I said bitterly. "It's just chicken pox or measles, or both."

"We should get dressed," said Gogo, "and go over to St. Vincent's Hospital."

"It's too cold out," I said, "and I couldn't walk. We should probably get something to eat. Some soup or something like that."

"There's no soup in the house," Gogo snapped.

"What is there?"

"Some canned spaghetti," she said.

I groaned again, sat down on the bed, leaned back, and said, "Please, Gogo, please share that rug."

We fell asleep, that time more soundly. We lost all track of day and night, and then I heard a distant thumping—a terrible distant thumping.

Is that my heart? I asked myself. Is that Gogo's heart? Are we sicker than we know?

But the thumping continued, far too erratic for even hearts stricken by the plague. Then somebody began not only to thump on the door, but to kick it.

"Oh, somebody's stopping by," I said. "Gogo, go answer it. I'm sick."

"I'm sicker," said Gogo. "Let them go away."

I called through the doorway. All of the doors had easy access to the hallway. You could call through any crack and make your needs known.

"Who is it?"

"Jeffrey. Open up; help me."

"Why?" I said. "What's the matter? Go away, Jeffrey; come back tomorrow. Gogo and I are sick. I think we've got the measles or the chicken pox."

"But you've got to help me. I won't bother you. Just give me a chair."

"What time is it?" I asked.

"Ten o'clock," said Jeffrey.

"When? Ten in the morning; ten at night?"

"Ten at night," answered Jeffrey.

"Well, why don't you go home and go to sleep?"

"My roommate won't let me," Jeffrey said.

"He's a drip," I managed to say. "Well, you can't sleep here. The landlady gets annoyed."

"I need care," said Jeffrey.

Now there was too much noise in the hallway. "Shut that bum up. Either let him in or let him out," called somebody from outside. "What kind of a place are you girls running?" somebody else cried.

"Peasants," muttered Gogo. "We're surrounded by peasants."

Even feverish, she wasn't really in the black hole of Calcutta at all. She was slipping into the Russian court. She was becoming the aristocrat, surrounded by peasants. It was easy to follow her imagination. The peasants upstairs were making a fabulous amount of noise.

"Come on in, Jeffrey," I said.

Then I pulled the rug from her and wrapped it around myself.

"Come on in. What's the matter?"

Jeffrey stood there, shivering.

"I'm sick," he said, whimpering. "I'm very sick."

"What's the matter?" I said, my eyes now opening up well enough to see him. Jeffrey had the measles too! Sick as he was, he wanted to share our rug.

"No, you don't," said Gogo. "That's my favorite blanket."

He seemed sicker than we were, and I watched his face carefully.

"We can't go out," I told him gently. "But if we wait here, somebody's bound to come home from the country or wherever they went on Sunday and stop by."

I had barely spoken when there was a discreet knock at the door again, a ladylike knock. It was Betty Lou.

"I was just stopping by to see how you girls were," said Betty Lou.

"You're a lifesaver, Betty Lou," I said.

I was not particularly fond of Betty Lou. She lived the kind of life I was running away from. She still lived with her parents, still had endless amounts of money, or so it seemed, still made inane remarks about our friends—knew nothing about printing, and, I decided, hadn't read a book since she left college.

"But, Betty Lou, don't come in," I added hurriedly. "We're contagious."

"Well, don't be dramatic," she said, with one of her rare instances of talking back.

"I mean it. Don't come in. I've got measles or chicken pox,

and Gogo's got measles or chicken pox or maybe worse, and Jeffrey's got something."

"What's Jeffrey doing here?" she whispered cautiously.

"Jeffrey's sick," I said. "He looks sicker than we do. I think he's got an awful fever, but I don't have a thermometer."

"Get a doctor," she said.

"There's no telephone. Have you forgotten?" I said.

"Okay," she said, "I'll go down to the drugstore and call for a doctor. Then I'll come down from Scarsdale in the morning."

"All we need is a doctor," I said. "The doctor will send us up some food from the delicatessen. Most doctors are very obliging."

"I'm sorry you girls don't feel well," commiserated Betty Lou, struggling to play the role of Florence Nightingale.

"Betty Lou," I told Gogo and Jeffrey, "is going to call the doctor for us."

"Will we get a special price?" Jeffrey wanted to know. "Would one doctor see us for a special price?"

"Oh, I'm sure," I said. "Now, everybody go back to bed."

We had made a bed for Jeffrey on the floor—large pillows, all of uneven sizes, but he didn't seem to care. He lay down and fell instantly asleep. Gogo and I had a minor tussle over the rug and fell asleep ourselves. Days went by, maybe years. In our imagination, it didn't matter. Eventually we heard a professional knock on the door. You can always tell a professional knock.

The doctor came in. He was an extremely nice fellow.

65

It was measles, all right, and yes, he would get the delicatessen to send up some of Magda's special chicken soup.

"Take it easy for a few days," he said. "Don't read too much, or do anything like that."

"But do us a favor," I said then, "when you send up the medicine, ask the drugstore to send up a pack of cards."

"Okay," said the doctor. His name was Bill. "Are the three of you used to getting contagious diseases together?"

"No," I said, smiling weakly.

Bill got to be a great friend in later years. But he said he'd never forget that first night. Joey had greeted him at the door, guarding our apartment like a dragon guarding fabulous Tennyson maidens. He was a little surprised to see Jeffrey, but he figured Jeffrey was probably a knight who had come to save us.

This whole idea made the apartment more bearable for us for a while. Gogo called it the Isle of Avalon, and that made it even look better.

Magda sent fresh soup up from the delicatessen each day.

We'll have a terrible bill, I thought, but Magda never charged us for it.

And Betty Lou returned, as she had promised. She rapped three times on the door, and Jeffrey, looking better but more disheveled, flung it open. There was no one there, but there was a package, and Joey, our lovable rat, had obviously made a brief try at getting through cellophane wrapping. It was one of those great bon voyage packages filled with fruits and nuts, a can of chicken soup, packages of mints.

"Somebody's left you a present," Jeffrey announced.

Gogo said, "Let's see."

The cold was vicious in the hall, as she tried to find a card. "It has to be Betty Lou," she said. "This is typical of Betty Lou."

"It's Scarsdale's answer to the measles," said Jeffrey.

"Florence Nightingale," I said bitterly, "has just left a little bit of herself in the Crimea."

Then we all grabbed for the basket.

printer's passion

We had forgotten the printing press. It kept in touch with us, sending bills from uptown, where it seemed to pine to be closer to us.

Now that we were ensconced in our ketchup quarters, it seemed only fair and decent that we find something respectable for the printing press. It could not stay with us. In effect, there was no cellar at all in our Barrow Street apartment, but rather a kind of rabbit and rat warren filled with old trunks and suitcases with faraway stickers upon them—leather that seemed to crumble into dust in the hand with old dreams and old journeys.

"The press would like it in the Village," said Gogo, "and besides, we ought to stop dreaming and start making some money with it."

"We'll find it a good home," I said. "In the meantime, let's go and have some coffee."

We went up the cellar stairs after our investigations below, hearing as we walked the scuttle of Joey. The sound had grown as comforting as that made by any other pet. Joey had greeted us each morning as we put the garbage out, looking alert. "Almost downright intelligent," said Gogo; "more," she sometimes added bitterly, "more intelligent than some of our friends."

That was unfair. Although it was true that many of our friends in the early morning looked a bit more disheveled than Joey, who seemed to be trim and almost sleek, fed as he was on our own private cuisine, which consisted at that point of various *spécialités de la maison,* all using the basic recipe of canned spaghetti.

"Ye gads," said Gogo, as she dumped the garbage that morning. "I loathe spaghetti. Only some dumb rat would eat it."

We never actually saw Joey eat in the hallway. But we did hear him rustle the paper bags as though he were some great wild animal of the jungle, tearing apart a rhino by a water hole. My humanitarian feelings went so far that I often thought perhaps I should put water out for Joey, but over the months these feelings changed, and instead I settled for a cat from our friend Mr. Maggo in the restaurant next door.

Because of our unfortunate kitchen arrangements—only one burner on the stove worked and that only when it chose to—it was easier to go and have coffee outside. So we went as usual that morning for our coffee and to discuss carefully and practically our problem of the printing press. She now had a name; she was feminine in nature, of course, and we called her Agatha, a name that tried to be beautiful, we thought, but was, like Agatha, big, clumsy, halting, and extremely non-professional.

Professional was the word for us. We would have none of the non-professional fooling around that so many neophyte printers settled for, printing stationery and throwaways. No, we dreamed of higher things. Of printing books that would rival the Golden Cockerel books of England, the Nonesuch, the Colt books out in California, even the Peter Pauper Press. They had to be professional and handsome, and setting type itself, although we did it so laboriously, began to give us great pleasure.

We could not afford to make another mistake with Agatha. We had too little money. This time when we moved her, she had to stay put.

On our way to Riker's, we ran into Romany Marie, glowing as she always was, in a very fancy gown and full of conversation.

"You want to look at a new apartment, girls?" she said.

"Yes," said Gogo, "but this one has got to have a place for the printing press."

"I like to see spunk in girls," said Romany Marie. "That's the way the Village used to be in the twenties, when there was good printing going on here—and good poetry. Now it's a lot of nonsense. A lot of nonsense and a lot of tourists."

We felt uncomfortable for a minute. Did she still consider us tourists? We had been in the Village all of six months. We were old-timers, for sure. Certainly not bourgeois. We had no intention of ever leaving, and Gogo used to say that when we got married, we'd have our children here and they could go to the Park and grow up to be decent bohemians.

I wasn't sure what a decent bohemian was. For that matter, I was a little vague as to what an indecent bohemian was. But I thought an indecent bohemian was one who never bathed, while the rest of the bohemian aristocracy, on my own private measuring stick, was more or less adjusted to water.

Romany Marie, of course, was a true bohemian. She was also an extremely good-natured soul. She looked just the way she should look, her clothes bright enough, the jewelry colorful enough, the memories of the twenties not so far away or so overwhelming that she could not still be "a character," which she remained, of course, until she died.

"I need a new apartment myself," said Marie.

We had often wondered where she lived. Because of her name, we had speculated that she might live in a store front along with a group of gypsies. But she was gypsy in name only. Practical and pragmatic, warmhearted and hardheaded, Marie obviously had to live in an apartment, and it was our guess that she'd select a good one. Any house that Romany Marie looked at was well looked at.

"What I thought I'd do," she said, "was get a large apartment and cut it up, and you girls could have part of it."

Romany Marie obviously had suggested this to other people,
but it seemed extremely exciting to us, and we said yes, we'd go
see whatever she had to offer.

"Of course," said Gogo, "we mustn't forget Agatha."

"Oh, three of you won't matter," said Marie, "the more the
merrier."

"Yes," said Gogo, "but you forget Agatha's a printing
press."

That startled Marie, but for only a moment.

"Well, there should be a cellar," she said, "and if there isn't
a cellar, maybe there's a small room; and if there isn't a small
room, maybe we could put it in the hallway. If there isn't a
hallway, maybe I could get it somewhere in the restaurant."

She always had a restaurant of some kind, but I couldn't see
that the press would add any decorative quality to any restaurant. The restaurants in the Village in those days were still
decorated in pre-World War fashion. The jackets of books still
decorate the walls of Chumley's on Bedford Street, but the
jackets then looked newer, fresher; the photographs of the au-
thors on the back were not so weather-beaten, defeated, old,
and twentyish, as they were to become in later years.

"It wouldn't make much of a decoration for the restaurant,"
I said.

"You never know," said Marie. "You never know what
tourists are going to go for. Besides, so much of it is soldiers

74

and sailors these days," she said. "It'd be good to have a couple of soldiers and sailors around—mechanical-minded ones who could fix the press if something went wrong."

That was the kind of practicality that impressed me so in Romany Marie. I said no more until we saw the apartment. The whole idea failed then and there. The apartment was really only one large room, and though we all might have lived happily with Romany Marie, recalling the memories of her golden days in the twenties, we simply did not have the money to convert the huge room into two apartments.

Marie, however, continued to be a good friend. She greeted us each morning on the street, sweetly asking if we were getting enough sunlight. As winter progressed, of course, the sunlight crept at an angle, not into our rooms, but whimsically onto our fire escape.

Soon winter closed in, a winter such as might have frightened Robert Scott at the Antarctic, that might have challenged Peary at the Arctic. Our lights flickered all winter long. Joey hovered in the cold in the morning, because the furnace broke down consistently and then completely.

We sat around and read during those winter nights, bundled up in coats and scarves. Gogo would arise in the middle of the night and thrash about. It was difficult for me to figure out how she could thrash about with our simple furniture. But that she did, and I discovered morning after morning that she had pulled up the rug and was snuggled underneath it like a Saint Bernard dog.

Sometimes I would call her in the morning, carrying a cup of soup in my freezing hand. She would reach one arm out, say "No, no," put her hand underneath the rug again, and try to go back to sleep.

This happened rarely. Ordinarily, she was the first to get up and, except in very cold weather, she started the day with a bang. The bang of pots and pans, because although we had decided to have our coffee outside, it seemed appropriate to pull out all the pots and pans before we started the day, to look at them speculatively, decide it wasn't worth the effort, put on our coats, and go to Riker's for coffee.

It was, of course, a completely different cup of coffee than the late-morning coffee of our free days. On workdays, we were just haggard members of the employed. We kept up the routine, cold and miserable, as long as we could, and then I said simply, "This is ridiculous. I'm sick of the bookshop. I don't get any time to read there, and then that weird thing happened back by the cookbooks."

A boy my age, having coffee beside me, picked up his ears. I tried to lower my voice, but it was impossible—Riker's is always so noisy at that time in the morning. I said, "You know, Gogo—what happened to Mrs. Able."

"Oh," said Gogo, "you mean when her womb fell back by the cookbooks."

"Yes," I said, lowering my voice. "I don't know quite what she meant. I don't suppose she picked it up or anything like that. But she's always threatened me that if I don't carry something for her, her womb's going to fall again. And I find it an awful burden. Besides," I added, belligerently, "you'd think in a bookshop, they'd let you read."

"What do you want out of life?" Gogo demanded. "They don't let me take photographs in the camera shop. All I'm getting out of it is varicose veins. Maybe we should both quit. What would we do, though?"

"Well, we've got Agatha."

"If we didn't have Agatha," said Gogo, "I don't think we'd be in this fix. Maybe we wouldn't have to take jobs we didn't like. Maybe we could be free. Why did we come to the Village if we're not going to be free to live? I don't care if I ever work uptown again. And look at all the money we'd save on subway fares."

"The only thing we can do," I said to Gogo, "is to get Agatha working commercially."

We thought this over. Somehow or other it was like saying to some of our friends who were forever painting endless canvases that perhaps they should try commercial art. That was a way to make enough money to pay for their coffee. And then Gogo and I, who were struggling so with the commercial world, would not have to invite them endlessly to our free dinners.

"I don't know about Agatha," said Gogo. "I don't know about handling her commercially either."

"I know. She's like a fine artist. She's temperamental. I don't think we'll ever really make a dime out of her. She's just big

77

and clumsy, and she's robbing us. She's like some great maw. She's tyrannical."

I was exhausted at my outburst, and the boy next to me turned and said, "Why do you want to have anything to do with a bum like that? Nice girls like you. Is she some woman preying on you nice girls?"

Gogo said to him, "Mind your own business."

But I said, "Oh, it's all right. Agatha's a printing press."

"A what?" he exclaimed.

"I said, a printing press. She's our printing press, and we have to get her down here to the Village and work her commercially."

My new friend, whose name turned out to be Max, said, "What do you girls know about printing presses?"

"Nothing," I said, "but we'll learn. And then we'll be fine printers."

"Except for the union help," Gogo added.

"Union help?" said the waitress. "Don't you girls go and be strikebreakers or anything."

But Max said, "Come on. Let's get out of here. I'll buy you both a cup of coffee somewhere else."

"We've got to go to work," said Gogo.

"You could take the day off, or be late," said Max.

"Well," said Gogo, looking at her watch, "there's a little time. Not much. Let's go next door and try the drugstore coffee."

So we did, and Max told us about Manuel. The great thing

about the Village in those days was that there was always a Jeffrey knowing about apartments, there was always a Max who knew a Manuel, and so on.

Manuel, Max explained, was probably the greatest printer we would ever know in our life. Manuel was a Spaniard, from the north of Spain. Manuel's family had printed—here he waited for me to hold my breath, which I did appreciatively —Manuel's distant relatives had printed *Don Quixote.*

He let this sink in for a while. I couldn't think of a better introduction to Manuel.

"Besides," said Max, "his wife makes the best *arroz con pollo* in the Village. Also, he's not interested in girls. He won't be chasing you like that. He'll take a fatherly interest in you."

Gogo and I already had an extraordinary number of interested, fatherly figures knocking on our door. Fatherly interest, particularly of the kind that was found in the Village, seemed the last thing we wanted. But Manuel was different, said Max.

"Okay," I said, "let's talk to Manuel. Does he know how to run a platen press? She's a gentle press, she's delicate. Agatha is an unusual character."

"Manuel is very sensitive," said Max. "Very sensitive. I think I heard somebody say that he had printed some of Lorca's poetry. That should be enough for you. What else could you want?"

So we met Manuel.

don quixote of 14th street

I thought Manuel would be tall, an angular giant from La Mancha, a Don Quixote himself, but he was a short little fellow, very fast on his feet, and nimble with his hands. He could set type faster than anybody I knew. He was an anarchist; a Spanish anarchist. All artists, he said, should be anarchists, as should all great printers.

"Don't worry; I'll fix her up for you girls. You'll have a nice going concern here."

"You mean commercial concern?" I said. Finally, Agatha was going commercial.

"Absolutely," he said. "First we'll make the money; then we'll print the books."

I was to hear that same comment made, throughout all my

years of publishing, by financial, rather than artistic, adventurers. But at that point, Gogo and I had barely a hundred dollars between us, and we were both determined to give up the captive life of going to work uptown, so the promise of commerce seemed great. We had already lined up the volumes of poetry we would publish. Robert Duncan had given us some; there was a promise of poetry by Kenneth Patchen, a pamphlet from Henry Miller, and material from other writers of equal stature. What no one had promised us was any commercial work. We did not even know how we would get it.

Manuel said, "Don't worry. I'll bring in dignified, respectable work."

We used fifty dollars to hire one of the extraordinary trucking concerns of the Village. It is not, of course, a trucking concern at all, but a fleet of wagons out of Downing Street manned by the most pathetic derelicts who, for small sums, will collect newspapers, tin cans, or any other treasures.

Manuel, with his skillful hands, took the press apart satisfactorily enough for it to be put in two of these wagons, and they were trundled down by foot from uptown. We thought of accompanying all the pieces, but we only reached Seventy-second Street.

"Too nerve-racking," said Gogo.

It looked as though the whole machine would be catapulted out of the wagon when it reached midtown.

"And how will you get it through the garment district?" I

said. Somehow or other, the garment district was always a world to be approached cautiously. You might lose everything in that skelter of clothing racks and fur coats.

"Who would want Agatha?" said Gogo. "Nobody's going to steal her."

"No," I said, "but maybe we'll get a ticket of some kind. I don't know whether you can carry printing presses through the streets of New York in those great big wheelbarrows."

"Let them handle it," said Gogo, showing her true administrative ability. And we got into the Seventy-second Street subway, heavy of heart and a great deal lighter in purse.

Just as Max had found us Manuel, Manuel found us Polychronos. Polychronos was a Greek, and Polychronos knew all available loft space in the Village. Or so Manuel told us. Or so Polychronos told Manuel.

We settled on a place that brought back memories to Gogo and me of our grandfather's coffee business in lower Manhattan. The first floor was a coffee shop filled with coffee beans of all sizes, the spirit of enterprise weak in the owner but his product delicious and penetrating as it wafted up through the floorboards to where we had put Agatha in all her new-blown commercial beauty.

Manuel now had taken her apart, put her back together again, oiled her and greased her, polished her and patted her, until she looked like some sleek computer that would tabulate, record, and take charge of our life.

Our problems with Agatha were now well known in the

Village. It didn't surprise us to have somebody whom we didn't know come up and say, "I have a little something for Agatha," and press in our hands a sheaf of rather wretched poetry or occasionally fifty pages of what would be the great American novel. Novelists rarely approached us, however. They knew that our printing skills were still negligible and it would take longer for us to print a novel than it took Proust or Joyce to write one. But the poetry was omnipresent; they gave it to us everywhere—in Riker's, they left it for us in the drugstore, they put it in the mailbox, they became acquainted with Manuel and shoved it in his breast pocket as he stood waiting for the lights to change at the corner of Eighth Street.

"I didn't know there was so much poetry in all the world," said Gogo.

"There isn't. Not good poetry," I said, "and when we publish poetry, it's going to be good."

"I'm beginning to wish they'd press a little something into our hands that isn't art," said Gogo. "Money, for example; we're going broke."

And we were. But Manuel saved the day. He came into the apartment one evening after having worked hard all day. He had another job, of course; he could not work for us completely.

He said, "I have the first piece of work for you girls; the first commercial work for your machine. It's beautiful. You're in business."

"I hope," said Gogo, "it isn't letterheads."

"I hope you're not just inscribing names on people's Christmas cards," I said.

"Nope," said Manuel. "This is beautiful. It's the closest thing to printing in gold."

We were startled now. Our budget could not afford anything printed in gold; even gold stamping was going to be quite beyond us if we ever reached the point where we bound those little pages of poetry that we were occasionally getting off the press.

"Here it is," said Manuel. And he unwrapped our first venture.

Our great dreams turned to ashes, but even the ashes were well placed because for her first job our great Agatha had surprinted the names of local bars on aluminum-backed ashtrays.

"They're great," said Manuel. "Aren't they great?"

"Oh, they're great," I said. "Of course, they're not art, but they're great."

"Oh, they're great," said Gogo. "Just great. There go our hopes into ashes."

Manuel grew slightly uncomfortable. "Well, we're making money," he said.

"That's good," said Gogo. "How much do you think we made this week?"

Our man from La Mancha, our Don Quixote of typesetting, said simply, "Well, we only lost five dollars. What do you expect? We're just starting."

"What do you expect?" Gogo said, turning to me.

"What do you expect?" I said, turning to Gogo.

And then we all had a cup of very black coffee, using Agatha's ashtrays for saucers. They leaked, of course; but you can't have Limoges china and commerce at the same time.

the taste of chili

Spanish anarchists taught us to cook. Manuel, after working at the press, would occasionally come over for our excellent dinners. We varied our canned spaghetti with at least a reasonably excellent salad, because the greens of Bleecker Street were so enticing.

"This can't go on," he said.

"What? The press?" I asked, suspecting that it could not.

"No; this kind of food. You'll all die. You must get Luisa to teach you to cook."

"I'm willing," said Gogo. "When shall we start?"

"Sunday," said Manuel. "Come Sunday. She'll have all Sunday with hardly anything to do. She doesn't work on Sunday, and she'll have only six children. Eduardo will be away. We have seven boys."

"Oh, I wouldn't want to interrupt Luisa's free day," said Gogo, looking at me. Was he quite sure that Luisa had nothing to do?

"Sunday's a good family day," said Manuel. "Come Sunday."

"Should we bring something?" I asked.

"Some fresh coffee beans," said Manuel. "Some food stamps if you have them. But we Spaniards know how to spread our meat. Come Sunday, and bring an appetite."

Fourteenth Street then, as now, was the dividing line of the Village. Actually, only the downtown streets seemed to us at all Villagy. Once across Fourteenth on the uptown side, the world was already changing. It was not the Village. It was an outpost, outskirts for some world of commerce and conformity that we would have none of. The downtown side of Fourteenth Street was something quite different. Between Seventh and Eighth Avenues, when we were young in the Village, there was a Spanish colony—not a Puerto Rican but a Spanish colony—speaking often a Spanish as pure and beautiful as the women, as golden as saffron. The very Spanish they spoke depended, of course, on where they were from. There was a Spanish as rough as the Spanish blankets in some apartments; language as mellifluous as honey in others.

We arrived that first Sunday in happy expectation. At the door, Gogo said, "I haven't had a Sunday dinner since we left home. Sunday dinner always seemed so square to me. Well, I'd rather have Sunday dinner now than anything."

"Of course, it won't be the same kind of Sunday dinner as at home," I told her. "But it is a nice feeling. Sunday's a good day in the Village."

"Not," said Gogo, "if you're fixing canned spaghetti."

We knocked on the door, but before the final tap Luisa opened the door, and we nearly fell into the room. The door was almost the same vintage as our door and suffered from the same arthritic condition. It never properly shut, and as a result when it opened it was nearly torn from its hinges.

"Good, good," said Luisa. "Good, good, we start to teach you to cook now. We start and then we eat."

It was a large loft-type apartment, separated into rooms with hanging blankets. The apartment was chilly, but there was a charcoal burner at one end of the room, giving off a fragrant and exciting odor. The other end consisted of the kitchen, and there were five small children hovering around the stove, one old gentleman with his feet up on the table, and two other guests, gentlemen both, whom Luisa introduced. One was Don Carlos, a Latin American psychoanalyst; the other was Don Paola, a famous Latin American composer; and the old gentleman was one of the many Spanish painters that had studios on Fourth Avenue close to Klein's. They did not sit, but moved around constantly throughout the loft, pushing aside the blankets, looking out of the windows onto the excitement of Fourteenth Street below, smelling the herbs that Luisa was crushing, and addressing Gogo and me in superb Spanish or poor English. As the afternoon progressed, everyone stood in line to take samples from Luisa's cavernous pots, from her shallow pans, from her plates, from her oven, and from her corner table that overflowed with color.

"Luisa is the greatest cook on Fourteenth Street," said Don Carlos. "Her family were cooks for the family of Don Quixote."

"Oh," I said, with interest, "it's astonishing that the printer of Don Quixote and the cook of Don Quixote should get together this way."

"I don't know about any such printer," said Don Carlos.

"That's how I was introduced to Manuel," I said. "His family printed *Don Quixote,* I had heard."

"Perhaps an illusion," said Don Paola, kindly. "Spaniards from La Mancha often suffer from illusions."

"Hunger and disillusion," said the Spanish painter.

"One needs the south," said Don Carlos. "The hills of the Sierra Nevada, the country around Granada for great poetry, for great music, for great perfume."

"On, on, on, they talk," Luisa said to me. "My English is good, no?"

"Excellent," I said. "You all speak excellent English. I like the sound of Spanish though. I speak it poorly, but we understand it well enough. It seems an extremely comforting language."

"Oh, Spanish comforts enough," said Luisa. "But it's cruel too. Sometimes we are crucified on our own words. What is politics but a crucification? Is that the right word, Don Carlos? A crucification of the vocabulary."

"I'm hungry," said Don Carlos.

"He talks to crazy people," Luisa interjected.

"Oh, that's not what an analyst is," I said.

"No?" she said. "But just looking at his smile makes you feel nice. Such a nice smile. He should have been an anarchist."

"I've never seen many smiling anarchists," Don Carlos told her.

"That's what we need," said Luisa. "We need a smiling anarchist. Manuel is going to talk to Don Carlos. You girls should become anarchists. It's much better than being Presbyterians."

"I guess," I said, thoughtfully, "you can be a Presbyterian and an anarchist."

"Oh, no," said Luisa, "never." And then she roared with laughter.

She could cook as easily as she could talk, and her cooking and talking were all part of the same thing.

"Home," she said, "I give them a little bit of home here, the taste of home. For the Mexicans, I am a taste of chili; for the Chileans, I have the taste of empanadas; for those from Barcelona, I make a great paella. A taste of home. That's what you must always give them. Even when you marry. Give them a taste of home."

"All the guys we know," said Gogo, "must have been raised in Riker's. That's the only taste of home they seem to be interested in."

"It's a good idea, though," I said, adding saffron to one of

Luisa's pots. And I could see myself married to some strange and interesting man from La Mancha; not, however, an anarchist, but some gay, smiling Presbyterian Spaniard from La Mancha.

"Watch out," said Luisa. "That's too much saffron."

"Oh," I said dreamily, licking it from my fingers and finding it slightly bitter.

"Too pungent, too much—too much of the taste of home and everybody gets sick."

The analyst smiled. Light shone into the room, and at the window that looked down at Fourteenth Street, the painter was sketching quietly, sketching for himself, not for the world.

"He paints street lights," Luisa said, "only street lights. Street lights in the morning at ten o'clock, street lights in the morning at eleven o'clock, street lights at noon. He has painted 972 street lights."

"You mean real street lights?" I said. "Out on the street? Does he work for the city?"

"Oh, no," she said, shocked. "He is an artist. He only paints street lights inside. You know, paintings of street lights. Magnificent, superb street lights. He is probably the greatest street-light painter in the world."

"Hawthorne maintained that you could look at someone under a street light and imagine a story from the light shining on his face," I said.

"Hawthorne?" said the analyst, picking up his ears. "Great writer, great writer."

"My English is good for talking," said Luisa, "but books in English are funny."

"Oh, you'd like Hawthorne," I said. "He's kind of dark and romantic," and then as I thought about it, Spanish, too. "He's kind of Spanish in the way he looks at the world."

"Oh, he's an anarchist," said Luisa.

"No," I said. "You certainly couldn't call him an anarchist."

"I bet," said Luisa, with satisfaction, "his wife couldn't cook like this."

"Few wives could," I said.

The children had watched us quietly long enough. They went into the center of the room now, between two hanging rugs that turned out to be their section of the loft, and put on a phonograph. The sound filled the room.

"Green. Oh, how I love you, green." It was somebody reading one of Lorca's last poems.

"Too much sadness," called Luisa to the children. "Not that for a Sunday. Put on some flamenco."

But the children waited patiently, listening to the phonograph, listening to that voice far away and now dead. They waited until the end, and then the oldest turned the machine off with a sigh.

"A minute," the analyst said, "a minute between Lorca and the flamenco."

"Lorca," said Luisa, "should have been a true anarchist, but he had something Presbyterian about him." She looked pointedly at me.

"Oh, I can tell," Luisa continued. "I can always tell a Presbyterian."

The Presbyterian Sundays of our childhood now had another impression superimposed upon them. A Spanish anarchist Sunday, scented with strange and exotic spices. Instead of our leg of lamb, with which we had grown up, we now had chorizo—an aggressive sausage—beans such as New England would never know, and pickles and peppers which had never seen the green fields of New Jersey.

"God moves among the pots and pans," said Luisa.

"St. Theresa," I said. "I know that's a quote from St. Theresa."

"St. Theresa, nothing," Luisa scoffed. "My mother said that, I say that, my children will say that. Not only God, but the children move among the pots and pans."

Pans fell, dishes clattered, laughter brushed against the hanging rugs. A whole winter of anarchist Sundays went by, filled with the strange light of sunshine coming through the uncurtained windows, brushing through the sides of the hanging blankets. Dried red peppers hung from the walls, loaves of bread were offerings upon the table. The chairs and the ironing board were festooned with drying herbs; kidney beans were scattered across the floor, and the children played jacks with them. Occasionally somebody desperate would appear in the loft—a punch-drunk, bantam-weight prize fighter from the north of Spain or a bullfighter who had lost his first fight.

"Do not matter, do not matter," Luisa told the bullfighter.

"All bulls are really Presbyterians. You are a kind anarchist at heart. You cannot kill even the downtrodden bull."

She doled out beans and comfort, chicken and advice. She brewed up the pleasures of Sunday, and gave for a while another home—a Spanish home.

We thought seriously of becoming anarchists.

"It would never work, Seon," said Gogo. "She's right, you know, about our being Presbyterians. A Presbyterian anarchist is crazy. They don't go together."

As spring came, we had an enormous repertoire of dishes, and a new collection of pots and pans of different shapes and sizes. We no longer went out for breakfast. It was great to start the day with a bowl of chili.

the search for light

If the Spanish anarchists taught us to cook, one Greek of the community taught us to suffer.

"Noble suffering," said Gogo. "The Greeks suffer nobly, and they have to pass it on to us."

Our Greek landlord wasn't satisfied with the discomforts that we suffered in our present apartment. No, he had greater plans for us.

"Watch out," said Gogo. "He'll pluck out our eyes."

"That was Oedipus," I said.

"He'll do something. Watch out," repeated Gogo. "Whenever he comes up and says, 'I have a nice new apartment for you girls,' I know what he means. He means that he wants us to suffer straight out of the *Odyssey*. He wants us to be like Homer, going from place to place, apartment to apartment."

"Maybe he's sincere," I said. "You know you have to keep looking until you find the ideal apartment."

"Don't be ridiculous," she said. "You sound like *House and Garden*."

"I'm not looking for an ideal apartment. I just want one without rats. And is it too much to ask for just a little light, just a little, tiny light?"

Gogo had surprised us all, and obtained a new job uptown that she liked very much. It was a war job, and she was very secretive about it. Max decided that she was a secret agent of some kind. I knew, however, that she was really handling steel purchasing, but that seemed equally fascinating. Gogo's new respectability with her uptown job meant, however, that she needed a more respectable place to call home.

"In the first place, this isn't an apartment," said Gogo. "It's a cave."

"Oh," I said. I realized she had gone far beyond the point at which it had been the black hole of Calcutta. Uptown was beginning to get to her. Crossing over Fourteenth Street was changing her personality. I looked at her suspiciously.

"What do you mean, a cave?"

"It's some cave out of the *Odyssey*—that's what it is. Or like a cave in Scandinavia. Anything could happen in this apartment. The only trouble is that while anything could happen here, you couldn't see it. It's too dark. There could be murders. All of the anarchists could make plans to blow up all of Europe, but we wouldn't know it. We couldn't see them."

"Well, we could hear them," I said.

"How could you hear them?" said Gogo. "They make so much noise upstairs, I can hardly hear you now."

She threw open the window. "And listen to that."

Across the way, our neighbor was playing his record. He had but one record—one single record which contained three Gregorian chants. He had been playing the record for six months now.

"I wonder," said Gogo, "if it's similar to what we learned about Bishop Berkeley at school; that if you're not here to hear that record, it doesn't exist. Do you think it's some kind of philosophical problem?"

"It's just noise," I said, slamming the window. "You're edgy. Uptown is getting to you. Don't conform too much."

"Don't conform too much?" Gogo was indignant. "Just because I want to see if there's a sky out there?"

"All right. I'll go to work and buy the extras. You find us another apartment."

That Monday was glorious. Gogo was up at the crack of dawn. She left now unbearably early in the morning. I had fed her sweetly on a dish of fragrant, leftover chili, but she was moaning now about it.

"First we have a life filled with canned spaghetti; now we have chili for breakfast. I don't think it's respectable. I don't think I should go into the office smelling of chili."

"Oh, they won't know what you smell of," I said kindly.

"None of them have had chili for breakfast. They couldn't identify it."

"Well, they do an awful lot of sniffing," said Gogo. "Besides, they don't trust me anyway, coming from the Village."

"Oh, tell them you're just stopping by on the way to Scarsdale," I said bitterly. "Don't let them get at you, Gogo. Don't conform too much."

"*You* just better get that apartment," she said. "Now, Seon, remember, this time use your head. For a smart sister, you're the dumbest apartment-getter I've ever seen."

It was true that I probably saw all apartments somewhat too romantically. I did not know how to evaluate either rats, leaky faucets, or plumbing. I didn't even really know how to go about finding an apartment, except by that ambiguous phrase which was common in the Village, "word of mouth." I did everything by word of mouth; my own words and the words of my friends. I had new friends all over the Village, all eager to give me advice, poetry, recipes. I now had an excellent recipe for curry, which I occasionally tried out on Gogo at breakfast. And I had inside information about apartments.

The best information about apartments, I discovered—and perhaps that was the reason that my apartment-hunting was sometimes disastrous—was to be obtained over coffee. You never knew who would have some bit of advice, know of an opening, know whose book was going to be published, whose piece of music was going to be performed, whose paintings

would be shown, know who was conforming and moving uptown, who was depressed and defeated and moving out of
town, or who just wanted a change.

"Gogo simply wants a little light," I told Jeffrey.

"I don't think I'd better get into this," said Jeffrey. "She's
always suspicious of me, particularly when I mention apartments. I believe she thinks I'm in the real estate business."

"Aren't you?" I said somewhat bitterly. "Didn't you get a
rake-off on our present apartment?"

"That's an awful thing to say," said Jeffrey. "All I got was
that old bookcase that someone had left behind. I'll tell you
what. I'll help you get an apartment without any strings at-
tached, and then you'll make me some chili at your new apartment."

"That's not much of a promise," I said.

"Well," said Jeffrey, "there are two ways to get an apartment. One's by word of mouth, and the other's to look."

"Where shall we look?" I said. "There are thousands and
thousands of apartments."

"Probably word of mouth is the best to start with," said
Jeffrey. "Meet me here tomorow and I'll have some news."

That evening Gogo said her feet hurt. Her feet hurt and she
said she smelled of chili all day, and, no, she wouldn't eat curry
for breakfast.

"You're out of your mind," she said. "You've gone Village."

"You've gone uptown," I said.

"How's the apartment coming? I'm not going to live in this cave. You can live in this cave all by yourself."

"Wait until tomorrow night," I said. "I'll have some good news tomorrow night."

"Oh, my feet hurt," said Gogo. "You do too much standing around in an office."

"I can't feel too sorry for you," I said bitterly. "At least you get lunch."

"You had lunch," she said. "What did you have for lunch?"

"Chili."

"Oh, save us," she said, "and here we have it for dinner again."

"Well, you're not very inspiring to cook for when you're cranky. I'll make something different for breakfast."

"What, for instance?" she asked.

"I could poach an egg in the chili."

She hit me with a sofa pillow and went into the bedroom.

Jeffrey did have news the next day.

"It sounds perfect, Seon," he said. "It sounds like the most perfect apartment you're ever likely to get. It's got plenty of light, and not only that but you'll never guess."

"What?" I said. "Has Joey, the rat, moved over there?"

"No."

"Well, I can't guess what would be so special then."

"It's got a skylight," he said.

"A skylight?" I was interested. "Gogo will love that. She's always wanted a skylight. I think she ought to quit going uptown, and stay home now and paint portraits again. That would be perfect for her. I'll tell her to quit her job. I don't like her to turn bitter when she's so young."

"You're funny," said Jeffrey. "Don't you think you'd better take a look at it first?"

"Who told you about it?" I said trustingly.

"Polychronos, your landlord."

"Oh, Polychronos is a good fellow," I said. "He wouldn't want to lie to us. If it's got a skylight, it's got a skylight. Is it clean?"

"Yes," he said, "it's relatively clean."

"What do you mean, relatively?"

"Well, you know, it's clean. They're going to paint it."

"We'll wait until they paint it," I said, "but I'll put some money down on it. It'll make Gogo feel better."

"What do you feel? That it's bad luck to look at an apartment first?"

"Well, if it's as good as you say, then somebody's going to grab it," I said. "Let's go and put some money down on it."

I did put some money on it, and I called Gogo at her office. I said, "Gogo, do you really like working uptown?"

"No," she said, "it's rotten. I don't like it at all. I'm sorry I've been cross to you. I don't really mind chili and poached eggs for breakfast, Seon, but I hate working uptown. Why?"

I said, "Gogo, I'll work uptown for a while. You come down and paint."

"We've got no place to paint," she said. "I can't even see an easel in that room."

"You don't have to," I said. "I've just put money down on a glorious new apartment. It's got a skylight."

"It's got a what?" Gogo sounded excited.

"I said it's got a skylight."

"That's great," she said. "That's great. I'll quit today. I think it'd do me good to paint for a while."

"Good. Come home early," I said.

"What's for dinner?"

"You know," I answered.

"I think we'd better go to Riker's."

We celebrated at Riker's, still not having seen the apartment.

"I'd rather you didn't see it, Gogo, until they paint it. They're going to paint it by next Monday. So let's just gather all our things together and you spend the rest of the week getting all your painting supplies. I'll go look for a job."

I looked for a job. I had my hair cut; that always seemed to be like preparing myself for some great activity. And I got a job. Bookshops existed all over the city, and I could fit in any one of them comfortably. I knew books, and I liked people who liked to read. I could tell when people came in from the street whether they were planning to buy, whether they were just going to look, or whether they were just going to slip their shoes off and nurse their feet for a few minutes. I liked all of them.

I only worked half a week, that week, but the fifteen dollars seemed extraordinary. So we celebrated at Riker's again on Sunday night, and on Monday morning we went to look at our new apartment.

One had to agree it was light. It was light even on the outside. It was all the way over by the Hudson River, and the light that comes from the Hudson has a special quality. Of course, immediately under the elevated train tracks where our apartment house was located, it seemed neither light nor quiet.

"But, after all, the trains don't run every day," I said to Gogo.

"No," said Gogo somewhat suspiciously. "But, jeepers, this is a long climb up."

"Well, we wanted light," I said. "I figured if we got into taller buildings, we'd do better."

"How tall is this building? I thought it was against the law to make people walk up thirty stories."

"It's not thirty stories," I protested. "It's certainly not more than eight."

"Walking up and down eight stories. You must be out of your mind, Seon."

Not only was the building unusually high for the Village, it had an extraordinary ingress and egress, as Jeffrey called it. You walked up the steps to one flight, then had to go out on a precarious balcony, through a doorway again, up another flight, out onto a balcony, et cetera.

"All this is fine," said Gogo, "but what happens in the rain?"

"You get wet," I said. "It'll do you good. We used to like to walk in the rain as kids."

"I'm getting older every minute," said Gogo. "With every single one of these steps I take up this building, I'm getting older. I'm going to be a hundred years old by the time I get to the top. And the snow," she added, "can you imagine slipping out there on those little terraces every day in the snow?"

"Gogo," I said, "you haven't even seen it. You haven't given the apartment a chance."

"Did you see it?" But she was so busy groaning that I didn't have to answer.

We put the key in the lock.

"Look," I said, "a regular door and a regular lock."

We put the key in the lock and pushed the door. The door did not push.

"Well," I said, "that's funny. At least the door isn't hanging on its hinges."

"Give it another push," ordered Gogo.

We both threw ourselves against it. It didn't move at all. A gentleman from across the hall, weighing some four hundred pounds in his undershirt, came out and looked at us.

"Visiting somebody?"

"No," I said, "this is our new apartment. But we can't get in. We have a key, but we can't get in."

"Here, let me help you," he said.

He threw his four hundred pounds against the door.

"I'm Jackson," he said. "Just call me Jackson."

"Okay, Jackson," I said. "What's the matter with it?"

"Just painted shut," he said. "I don't know how they did it. They must have painted it shut and then crawled out of the window."

"Down a hundred flights of stairs?" said Gogo.

"Fine old building," said Jackson. "Bugs, reasonably decent. Fine old building. Lots of light. Not too much noise."

"Yes," said Gogo impatiently, and we went inside.

It was light. Everything was light about it. Nice bright sunlight shone on the roaches that had been painted carefully. They were like Egyptian scarabs who could not get away, but were caught in movement on the kitchen cabinets.

"Quaint," said Gogo bitterly. "Quaint. Now you've gotten us one of those quaint places."

"Well, it's bright," I said. "You wanted something bright."

She looked around the first room, which was the kitchen, with a great cavernous tub of long ago, and then went into the living room. The living room was bright. Quite bright and enchanting, and if you bent over and looked underneath the railroad tracks that stretched in front, or stood on a chair and looked over them, you could even see the Hudson.

"River view," I said, "nobody mentioned the river view."

"Well, what about the skylight?" she said. "Where's the skylight? In the bedroom?"

"I don't think there's a bedroom," I said calmly.

"You don't think there's a bedroom?"

"No, we'll just have to use one of those couches that pull out. Anything," I said, "for a skylight."

"Well, where can the skylight be?"

She pushed me out of the way, and rushed into the only remaining room there. It was the bathroom, and there, stretched above the toilet and the bathtub, was a decrepit-looking skylight with three of its panes of glass already broken.

"What am I supposed to paint?" she asked sadly. "Toilet bowls? Am I supposed to be like Manuel's friend and be the world's most famous painter of toilet bowls?"

"Don't jump at conclusions, Gogo," I said. "It is cheery; you can always paint in the living room."

"Seon, did you look at this apartment before we got it?"

"Well, no," I said, "but you know there's such a race for apartments these days."

"Nobody's going to race up a hundred flights of stairs," said Gogo. "Except you."

"What do you mean? Aren't you staying?"

"I'll stay till the snow," said Gogo. "I'll stay till the snow, when we can both luxuriate in the ice packs. Is there hot water?"

"I'm not too sure," I said sheepishly.

"And the snow will come roaring down, and great blizzards will come over our feet and chill the backs of our necks, and

111

perhaps we'll even die in the bathtub. Frozen there. Frozen stiff in one's own bathtub."

"You've convinced me."

So we stayed just a month, and Gogo painted a portrait of a toilet bowl.

a corner of france

The next time I looked in the papers. There I found it—an appropriate ad. "Four French sisters have room for two girls, separate quarters, companionable kitchen."

What, I wondered, was a companionable kitchen? I was beginning to discover that kitchens were a very companionable place indeed, if one had the right companions. But what was a companionable kitchen? Many of the kitchens that I had seen in the Village were remarkably hostile. Some of them were pygmies, dooming everybody taller than four feet to a terrible Swiftian existence. One had to bend and twist and turn. One got wrapped in all the Lilliputian despair of a single burner, or a refrigerator under the sink, or a sink buried in a maze of pipes and rust and little secret crannies that had once meant something to tenants long ago and far away. There they had left a jam jar, a single broken flowerpot, the dust of old basil. And often, way in the back of a closet, a tulip bulb. Or was it an onion? One never knew. They left a little part of themselves in the Village they had loved and from which they had either departed in victory, left in chagrin, or moved on simply farther west, farther east.

"Where is this place?" said Gogo. "East or west?"

"It doesn't say," I answered. "But at least I'm not going by word of mouth. Certainly we ought to be able to get along with four French sisters."

"Maybe you will," she said, "but four French sisters seem to me almost as bad as a skylight over a toilet."

"Don't be so insular, Gogo," I retorted. "With France still at war, there's something sort of poignant and almost necessary about us seeking out four French sisters. Besides, I think that's the problem with us at the moment. Two sisters are almost one too many. Let's see how we each handle five."

"Five sisters," Gogo groaned. "Five sisters and just one of my own. Well, I'm game. Just so they don't live on the top floor."

And then she thought that over speculatively. "Just so they don't live on the top floor of an eight-story building."

They didn't live on the top floor of an eight-story building. They lived on the top floor of a four-story building, whose owners, two young men, were away at war. Nor were they girls. The oldest was a grandmother of young children in

France that she had never seen. Her name was Nicole. Then there was Renée, sprightly as a French bird—a bird with elaborate plumage that one might imagine getting ruffled as a nerve got ruffled in the daily tedium of living. And there was Irene, proper but deceptive in her placidity. Irene had nerves; we never saw Irene without a *tisane*—we learned later that this was an herb tea that she made from all sorts of dried spices and herbs. Later Gogo said that Irene could probably make a *tisane,* one suitable for some ailment or other, just from house dust. Finally, there was Diane.

It was Diane who greeted us at the door. "Oh, you're the girls who phoned," she said.

"We thought maybe we'd look at the quarters," I said.

"You'll like them," she said. "Now wait right here and Irene will make you a *tisane.* Those four flights of stairs are wicked."

"She's never climbed eight flights," Gogo whispered to me. "And what is a *tisane?*"

"One of those French herb drinks," I said. "Don't you remember that Poirot is always drinking them in Agatha Christie's books?"

Gogo's ears perked up. It was her first sign of interest. I could see that her imagination was taking over. She would not be living with four French sisters, but four versions of the modern detective. We would be solving some intricate mystery, sharing in the methodical supervision of crime that was Agatha Christie's specialty.

"Come into the salon," said Diane.

We still hesitated a moment. After all, we weren't sure that we wanted the quarters, as they called them, but one would not want to disappoint them.

"You must have had many inquiries," I said.

"Yes," said Nicole, "many, but not from sisters. We're the last of six. It would be nice to fill up the family constellation again."

I felt a little uncomfortable. I hadn't been planning to be a family constellation, simply a renter of what I hoped would be more comfortable than the average Village quarters.

The whole apartment was far different from any that we had ever seen in the Village. It was filled with heavy French provincial furniture. The kitchen itself was almost like a Norman kitchen. The pots and pans were a perfect *batterie de cuisine.* Over the kitchen hung a tantalizing smell of herbs. It reminded me immediately of my grandfather's loft, where old ladies were forever sifting and weighing and culling tea leaves from faraway corners of the world, instilling in my nostrils some strange scent that I was never to forget. Here, in a more abbreviated fashion, less sharp but in many ways more appealing, was a distant smell of camomile, a smell of summers long ago in Long Branch, New Jersey, when we were children. And like children now, we sat on the edge of the couch, the teacups shaking slightly in our hands.

We both sensed that this was not truly the Village, that here was conformity—a kind of family life even fiercer than any we had known. I jangled the cup in my hand, a beautiful Limoges

117

cup. I had not had a drink of tea of any kind from a Limoges cup in about ten years. Gogo looked far more assured. She held the cup casually as she did the jelly jars that had become teacups, coffee cups, water tumblers, and, upon occasion, button holders to us. I concentrated so on the Limoges that my wrist trembled and I spilled a drop; it went tumbling onto the edge of the saucer, and then down onto the couch. I hadn't observed the pattern of the couch too well, other than to see that it was tapestried—a white background with a heavy pattern. But as I looked at it now, I could see it was made of rich embroidery.

"It's no matter," said Nicole. "Don't worry, it's only Germany."

I looked closer at the pattern. It was indeed Germany. It was an elaborate embroidery of the map of Germany, punctuated by red marks carefully embroidered in red French knots.

"Can you do French knots?" Nicole asked.

"Yes," I said, like a child again talking to my grandmother. "I'm very good at French knots." Inwardly I groaned. Was not that the world I wanted to get away from, fine hems and French knots? How did they fit into the Village?

"We need good knotters," said Nicole. "This is Germany, of course. Germany is only good to sit upon."

"Even worse," said Diane. "We only give our bottoms to Germany. But on the dining-room table, we have our map of Paris. Come see it, girls. We need you. We're getting tired of all the endless French knots, all the battles, all the spots where

118

the Allies have stopped. Come and stay with us a while. You'll
enjoy it. Our kitchen will welcome you."

The quarters offered for rent were good, and we moved in.
"Les Girls," as we soon began to call them, gathered around us.
They seemed to be a bit too overwhelming, but after all, outside was the Village. Inside was what? Not Paris, because we
found out later none of them had ever been to Paris, but provincial France. They came from the little towns around the
French Riviera. They had left before the war to make a pleasure trip together, only to be caught in the United States and
unable to return because of the war. Their letters from home
came rarely, but when they did an air of excitement always
hung over the apartment. Afterwards, there were headaches,
painful headaches for the four sisters, and they were doctored
on *tisanes* of all kinds.

Gogo and I thought it wise to express our individuality
strongly from the very beginning. We each had a large room,
and glory of glories, there was a connecting bath. There was a
short hallway to the kitchen—the companionable kitchen
which we were all free to use. It was companionable, for
everyone shunned the living room, and we would all sit in the
kitchen, talking over our hopes for tomorrow, the end of the
war, the future ahead.

We often went shopping with the sisters, Gogo and I feeling very young and naive, almost like schoolgirls, trailing behind these suddenly knowledgeable women. If they were shy

at home, they were thoroughly self-assured on the street, as they marketed for meat on Sixth Avenue, as they trekked en masse, down Bleecker Street. They were well known on Bleecker Street.

"Here come the ladies. Here come the ladies. Ah, *signoras,*" Beatrice would shout as she saw them round the corner. "Today I have shallots, a pinch of dill, the best endive. Move away, man, move away. Can't you see the ladies want to buy?"

They were not big spenders. They bought endive not by the pound, but almost by the leaf. They chose their salad greens with expert care. And for them, and for them alone, Beatrice, who was the queen of the business life on Bleecker Street, saved a little something—a kumquat or two, a red banana, a small bunch of grapes, a perfect pear. We would return to the apartment with our bundles, only to sally out again to an area that they knew well, an area that I had known myself as a child when there was still a remarkable French colony in the Twenties. There they knew an old gentleman in a paper store who prepared in the back of his shop the *tisane* that they most liked. Then to a French druggist where there was something for the liver. Then to the Bazar Français, where we bought something gay and attractive for the kitchen. In those days, there were superb "seconds" in casseroles that lasted forever, and out of those "seconds," Les Girls evolved a kitchen magic that was superb.

Once, in the early days of our stay with them, when Petit-pas was still in existence, we all went together to a family party, as they called it in this French restaurant that had so much significance for Gogo and me. Here we had often gone with our grandparents. Here we had first seen William Butler Yeats's father, and the great poet himself, when we were small children. In an aura of white kidney beans and the pungent pleasure of pepper, the girls talked of home as we did—our homes so culturally different and yet alike, because the girls were Presbyterians. They were severe, Calvinistic Presbyterians, but unlike the Scots, a great deal of color had crept into their lives; not the grayness of oatmeal, but the color of pimientos; not the harshness of haggis, but the succulence of sweetbreads; not the arrogance of oatmeal cookies, but the delight of *madeleines;* not beef but veal; not mutton but that superb spring lamb, almost raw, a delight to the eye and the tongue.

For the companionship of their kitchen and the pleasure of their company, we paid very little, but still young, we found the situation binding too. Too much bound Les Girls to each other. Were we not ourselves perhaps too bound together? True, we had broken away from each other in college, but was it not time for each of us to seek her own identity? Nevertheless, Gogo and I would sit with them in the kitchen, embroidering French knots, marking the paths of the Allied troops on the large tablecloth that was to decorate the table just once.

"It will be only used," said Nicole, "when the Allies enter Paris. Then we shall have a party."

As we sat embroidering, the war had a reality that it had not

121

had before. It had concerned us, of course. We had friends who were in the fighting. There was rationing of meat, coffee, shoes, and other things; we rolled all our own cigarettes; we could get no decent stockings. But all the rest had been a little unreal, just as our first months in the Village had been a little unreal. It was all too different from the pace of college and the world we had known.

Now the world took on a terrible reality; of knots and cross-stitch, as though we were embroidering history in our minds. I had always suffered doing French knots. They made my fingers bloody, and I hated to wear a thimble. I had felt like some character out of a fairy tale, her blood dropping and from it some strange flower growing, but now the blood became the mark of some battle—the intricate and terrible embroidery of the Battle of the Bulge, the fantastic weaving in and out of all those marks of D-Day.

Nicole, who was a fine seamstress, sometimes made some fabulous strip of embroidery as a decoration. Irene embroidered pictures of the Paris that she had never seen, while Diane scalloped the edges with fine lace of her own design.

These four sisters had given us a kind of reality about the war, and at the same time, they themselves were unreal. They were fairy-tale sisters, and we would bring our friends in to have a cup of *tisane* with us or, on rare occasions when Nicole was eager to treat us, a superb bottle of Chambertin. She knew a source of good wine that she would not reveal, just as she knew some fabulous secrets of cooking. With our friends' ration stamps, she would prepare a feast, and after it was over we would sit around the kitchen table, Max or Jeffrey, Richard or Bob, fascinated by the woman's needlework that went on. The boys, their chairs tilted against the wall, watched in silence these embroiderers, almost like the Greek spinners of fate perhaps, working their way to Paris.

"By the time we get to the outskirts," said Irene, "the war will end."

"How much longer?" said Max. "How long will it go on at the rate of this embroidery?"

You could feel a little of the magic of that kitchen. It was not the generals who were determining the outcome or the immediate ending of the war; it was Nicole, Irene, Renée, Diane. When their embroidery reached a certain point, Paris would be taken. Paris would be French again, and for them, in any case, the war would be over.

Max had been wounded in training camp, severely enough that war was a thing of the past for him. Richard had been a conscientious objector, imprisoned for a while, but then later imprisoned only in his writing, as he tried to explain and extol why his position was the right one. Jeffrey had been turned down for medical reasons, but Nicole had said gently to him, "It is still your war." Only here in the kitchen of Les Girls did I feel the threat it had been to these boys. Now we could see that they were men, and when this almost insane embroidery was finished, other men would return, sewn up by surgeons, emblazoned with the painful finery of purple hearts.

The atmosphere of the Village changed. We met the French colony through Les Girls, or through the many exciting exiles who had been helped by the United States through the facilities of the Joint Distribution Committee, or through private assistance.

I worked then in the Gotham Book Mart, on Forty-seventh Street, and through our doors I sometimes felt came all of intellectual Paris: André Breton, his hair as wild as a mane; Chagall, gentle, his spirit almost diaphanous; Yves Tanguy, Max Ernst. Maria and Eugene Jolas of *Transition* came later, Maria having founded a school for French and English children in the South of France during the war.

The world of war and the world of exile seemed to go together. These people were exiles, but they spoke so superbly, their work transcended so much that the universality of the world struck me as remarkably rich.

Frances Steloff of the Gotham Book Mart gave all these great minds a home away from home, a place for them to stack their poetry, to place their books, to meet each other, to bring back the glory of Paris.

I used to tell Les Girls about my work. They thought it madly exotic; I who had never been to Paris was showing them some strange, mysterious Paris. It was the Paris I knew— a remarkable Paris in New York with these intellectuals in exile. Occasionally, one or two of the surrealists would come to visit the sisters and they, too, would be given *tisanes*. A great

124

painter would marvel at the strange, surrealistic tablecloth, but then he would go away to his own realities. After such visits, the sisters were lonelier than ever and embroidered with even greater concentration. I began to feel that there was almost a morbidity about their endless sewing, as there often is as one works on a book or a poem or any piece of art—that certain morbidity that must be transcended to write the next page, mold the next piece of clay, make the next stroke of paint. So we made progress, all of us—the girls, Gogo, Max, Jeffrey, Richard, Bob, and me; some kind of progress in either growing up or understanding more about the world or each other. How strange it should come, I thought, in the making of French knots rather than through some glorious discovery on the streets of the Village.

Finally, the great day came. Nicole put down her needle.

"Tomorrow," she said, "they will enter Paris."

Who were "they"? She had not thought, of course, that it would be the Russians first. The Russians and the Americans, like puppets, being controlled by Nicole in a brownstone house in the Village. But her needle stopped. Civilization entered Paris. The girls spread their tablecloth for our feast.

"We can wash," said Nicole, "the blood from our fingers. Tonight we will eat from this cloth, and tomorrow I will fold it away."

And so she did. For them, the war was over. For us, curiously enough, it seemed to be only beginning. Even when V-E Day came, and Washington Square was madly filled with people singing and dancing, the war in the Pacific hung on, more meaningful, more terrifying. But their war, the four French sisters' war, was over. They had folded it up and put it away with the tablecloth, for which Nicole had made a satin sachet. And although Les Girls long ago went back to France to die, that scent hangs on the air. It is the scent of courage.

the irish glory boy

The Village has always been divided into more sections than Caesar's Gaul, but until fairly recently, it was also divided into different national groups—all forming, however, the cohesive pattern of the Village itself.

There were the old Village families; they had lived here for many generations, tracing their history back to the settlers, Dutch and English, who followed the Indians. Our friend, Miss Alda Willis, was one of those, and she would give us tea on cold winter afternoons, serving up mementos of the past the way one might present crumbled cookies on a platter. An air of ancient days always hung about her living room, and she would sit there, ghoulishly sewing forget-me-nots on a long winding sheet that she said was the shroud she intended to be buried in. She had started to work on it as a young girl, but when we knew her, in her eighties, she was approaching her sewing with even more enthusiasm. She would rip out the embroidery of long ago and replace it with bright new colors, all the time gaily chattering to us or to her parrot, who was called Village Pete.

Everybody knew Village Pete. His cage was next to the window at street level, and children could put their fingers through the grill and give him a delicacy.

"Of course," said Miss Willis, "Pete isn't a true Villager. He wasn't born here. He was born in the tropics. But I wanted to make him feel at home so I named him Village Pete. He thinks he's a real Villager. I don't think a little white lie really hurts, do you, girls?"

Gogo and I would answer gamely that a little white lie didn't hurt, particularly if it was told to a parrot.

"But Village Pete isn't a parrot," Miss Willis would say knowingly. "Village Pete is a friend."

Of course not all of Miss Willis' generations of family had been born in the Village. Once the Village had been "uptown," a suburb of the city that rested in what is now the financial district of New York. People went up to "Greenwich" for the cleaner air and to be surrounded by the beautiful trees. Miss Willis loved trees, particularly Christmas trees, as was obvious by the one she kept in the living room. The Christmas tree had been there for a couple of years, permanently dried, with old-fashioned decorations hanging from the boughs that were completely bare of needles.

The country homes that had once been summer farms for the merchants of Wall Street became, after the yellow fever and plague hit lower Manhattan, a true place of refuge. And the Village, as we know it now, began to spring up. In 1811, Manhattan's streets were laid out in a checkerboard fashion, but the Village already contained paths and lanes, as well as little secret squares and pockets, and no effort was made to impose the pattern on it. Even today, in glorious abandon, West Fourth Street crosses West Eleventh Street without a care in the world for those who want numerical order. Some changes were made in the Village; by 1827, the old potter's field had been turned into a park, Washington Square Park, almost the heart of the Village.

Once again growing Manhattan ignored the Village: its streets and lanes were as bohemian as the people who were to walk them. There was no through avenue, and the Village was left alone, a little pocket of nonconformity as Manhattan stretched northward. The Village, however, has always had the Hudson River at its doorstep, and at one time it was the main port for transatlantic shipping. On those ships came the new Americans, the European immigrants, who were to respond to the delightful quality of the Village itself, as well as to the tenements that had sprung up, which allowed the struggling new Americans cheap housing. Some of the first came from Ireland, and the Village was known for a long time as the "Irish Ward." They were followed by Italians, by a small colony of French, a few Scots (who stubbornly chose their own area on what is now Sixteenth Street and so refused to be true Villagers), by Germans, by Russians, by Greeks, by Lithuanians, and by the Spaniards who set up the colony on Fourteenth Street that became for a while our second home.

By the time my sister and I moved to the Village all of these nationalities had been welded into the American fabric, but many of the older Villagers we knew had a history of the past that excited our imaginations and often touched our hearts. There was still a small Irish colony left, and it was while we were living close to the waterfront that we met Kevin O'Brien.

Kevin O'Brien's eyes fascinated me. They looked as though he had been walking in the rain nearly all his life and all the color and contrast had been washed out of them. I never knew if they looked different in the winter, because we rarely saw him during the long, cold months. But in the spring, Kevin came into his own, seeking out the soft Village sun as though it might wash the shadows of the past.

One day in each spring Kevin O'Brien was a hero. It was, however, just for one day a year, and for that reason, he had a right to his own private immortality and, like so many private immortalities, it was based on a public venture.

Kevin was always going home to Ireland. But before he went, and he told us this regularly each year, before he went, he would tell us once more of the Easter of 1916.

"Oh," wailed Kevin. "I remember those submarines, plowing through the Irish Sea during the First World War. I remember Childers himself running the guns on the Irish coast.

I remember Griffith, the fair man, laying near to death in Mount Joy Prison. But I remember," he said, "I remember more than anything, James Connolly."

I was fascinated by Kevin's stories of the Irish Uprising in 1917. I was working on a book about James Joyce, and he fed me tales with a brogue I remembered from my childhood. The story of James Connolly, the revolutionist, always haunted me, but I had only read about it. Kevin had been there, on the back streets of Dublin—streets that looked like the back streets of our Village.

"Only the air was fresher there," said Kevin, sniffing the aroma from the restaurant next door. "You never smelled garlic. Oh, what a sweet smell that Easter Sunday had."

On Easter afternoon, Kevin would sit on the brownstone porch of the past, aware always that this day celebrated the flowering of Ireland's independence.

There were other Irish in this neighborhood, but they dissipated all their excitement and their Irish-American infatuation for a romantic Ireland that was dead and gone, as Yeats said, in the St. Patrick's Day parade. Only Kevin sitting on that stone porch yearly re-created the Ireland he had left.

"Oh, it was a victory that Easter day," said Kevin. "People have tried to narrow it down and belittle it and make it small, and then all the Troubles made it appear less and less, made it confused around the edges, but it was a victory. It was a glorious victory!

"Twelve hundred men, women, and children," said Kevin,

"against the English Empire. Twelve hundred noble hearts struck down that Easter day, all of them struck down. I'll tell you how it was at Mount Street Bridge, one of those glorious bridges of our fair Dublin city. There stood two thousand English soldiers.

"There was only a small group of us. But for twelve hours —and I just a boy, just fourteen when I was at Mount Street Bridge—for twelve hours we held those soldiers at bay.

"They had me running up and down for supplies, giving first one and then the other a gun if their shots were going astray. Just five men, and one of them a boy, against two thousand English soldiers. I got away, I don't know how I got away, but running across the back streets, I finally got to the General Post Office. There I couldn't even get in. I got back across the street despite the fact that it was being swept with machine-gun bullets, like rain in Donegal.

"Suddenly the world seemed to cave in. A great body fell with force. It was James Connolly, God rest his soul. The Post Office was burning now and bullets nicked the street.

"I ran to Connolly. I took up the stretcher, the three other bearers were men and I was just a boy, but with a boy's way, I moved rapidly and swiftly. I thought I could save Connolly with my own strength.

" 'You'll be all right, sir,' I said, 'you'll be all right. It's a glorious victory for us.'

"The other bearers said, 'And you're a glory boy.'

"We could not talk much because we were out of breath

133

when we got to the other side of the street. It was a mob now, and it sucked me in and I lost Connolly. I lost him.

"If I had been able to stay there, I could have kept him alive, and if I had gone with him to the Castle, I could have breathed some of my life into him. But they took him, they took him to the Castle. He had a fine sense of humor, even then. He told stories, and he told one man he had gone into the Post Office when they were setting up for the battle just to buy a stamp. Connolly said he did not know what he was really buying was a revolution.

"Then they shot Connolly," said Kevin. "They shot him, and they had to shoot him sitting down, because with his wounds he couldn't stand up.

"They told me that he asked for me before he died and that he said, 'We cannot fail; those young boys will never forget.'

"I never have," said Kevin. "I never forget."

"It's time you did," said Miss Willis gently, after greeting us one Easter on the street. "It's time you did. Come home with me and have a cup of tea."

And the new Villager and the old Villager went in and talked about the past.

"We ought to call him Village Kevin," Miss Willis said to Gogo and me later. "It would make him feel more at home."

hunting for bread

On Saturdays, we always hunted bread. We did not simply go downstairs to buy a loaf of bread, but hunted for it—different types, shapes, colors, all over the Village.

We had seen enough of the Depression so that bread had a symbolic meaning for us. In our forays around the Village, we discovered that the first bread lines that had ever existed, those of the nineteenth century, had taken place on Twelfth Street, now a street looking rather superior and affluent, but then only tortured and unhappy. While we lived with Les Girls, we hunted French bread. They would go out with us, early in the morning, up to Eleventh Street to the little shop where they had fine croissants and even better bread—superb, magnificent French bread. On cool spring days, we would walk all the way over to what is now the East Village and get dark and dusky loaves of Russian bread.

"Man, of course," said Max, coming into our new apartment (we had moved again), "cannot live by bread alone."

"No?" said Gogo. "Well, if you're not hungry, Max, leave it for somebody else."

Max, in answer, would cut himself a great hunk of bread and salami, and a faraway look of happiness would come into his eyes and then linger like crumbs around his mouth.

Even after we moved away from Les Girls, they would occasionally bring us a delightful country paté, and we would sit around, stiff in our chairs instead of sitting on the floor as we did with our younger friends, spreading the paté delicately on the French bread.

Italy was primarily around our present apartment, and we stayed for a long while in the heart of the Italian quarter of the Village.

Bleecker Street was the street of musicians then. It seemed fitting later that Gian Carlo Menotti should write an opera entitled *The Saint of Bleecker Street,* because when we first came out of school Bleecker Street had still an old-world quality about it. The ladies walked sometimes two or three together, all in mourning as black as the almost black skin of the cherries in the pushcarts. And yet it was not by any means a street of mourning. It was a street filled with life; it teemed with life.

Then, in all the Village, there was only one good pizzeria,

137

John's. And on the days of great celebration, all of us would take ourselves into John's, where occasionally they would make a pizza to be sent away to some poor, lonely Bleecker Street boy fighting in Europe or in the South Pacific. I could not imagine how those pizzas arrived, but perhaps just a faint smell in the box, just the touch of basil, perhaps a smear of tomato on the cardboard was all one needed. Nostalgia was all around one on Bleecker Street, and it could be conveyed in a smell, in a color, in a sudden burst of language.

Once Max brought Joe Gould to the apartment, carrying, it seemed, Joe under one arm, and one of those elaborate Sicilian loaves under another.

"My treat," he shouted to us up the stairs, "and I've brought you another. Joe Gould."

Gogo and I groaned a little. We had run across "the Village character," Joe Gould, many times in the street and occasionally even Les Girls would have him up for a *tisane.* They felt he needed one, but Joe, who lived completely on handouts—primarily bread and ketchup—loathed *tisanes.* He would die from a *tisane,* surely, he finally said, and the girls considered him ungrateful. Joe, of course, was always ungrateful. He was ungrateful for the way the world existed, ungrateful for whatever you might do for him, ungrateful for the possibilities of the hereafter, ungrateful to his ancestors, to the Harvard that had taught him, to the streets of New York which he walked. Mostly he was ungrateful to the Waldorf Cafeteria, whose ketchup he could drink in such quantity, and to the Jefferson Diner, which to all of us was almost a second home.

Joe muttered more than talked, moaned more than informed. He was working, of course, on what he called his "Oral History of the World" and in a copy of *Exile* magazine I had read the first section of what would be one of those monumental books of the twentieth century. In a way, Joe was the first of the happenings, like James Joyce himself. He said he would put everything in his book. The book would happen, would grow, would be a part of the organic rhythm of the life in the Village and the life around him and the life in the United States. Indeed, like Joyce, he was not only going to be a creature of the Village streets, of the Village city, but of the world, the universe.

In the meantime, he was just Joe, and he sat there for a while on the studio couch, mumbling and muttering, chomping on the Sicilian bread. I had brought out a bottle of ketchup, the way one might some rare old brandy, but Joe said simply, "Junk."

"There used to be good bread in Boston," said Joe, "right across the street from that church. You know the one I mean—the one where everything started."

"That was the garden of Eden," said Gogo wisely.

"No, that Boston church. In the Italian section," said Joe. "You know what I mean, Max. The one that Paul Revere hung the lights from."

139

"North Church," I said.

"Cruddy neighborhood," Joe muttered. "I don't live in cruddy neighborhoods because I want to. You hear a lot of good talk, though."

"Do you listen?" Max asked.

And then Joe, whose span of interest was amazingly short, jumped up, took the last of the bread, and clattered down the stairs.

"Have you hurt his feelings?" Gogo said.

"No, he's off hearing other voices," said Max.

"I'd like to see his manuscript," I remarked.

"I wouldn't advise it," said Max. "He's probably got it in a pile of boxes, and there may be rat turds and everything else mixed up with it."

"Maybe a vampire or bats," offered Gogo. "Joe sometimes reminds me of a vampire. He's sucking at anybody he can reach."

I knew that there wasn't anything really romantic about Joe. He was just pathetic. He was not yet the confused vagrant he was to become later. Every young person in the Village would at least try to treat him to a hamburger or a cup of coffee upon occasion, or if they were unusually brash, a piece of advice. None of us had any identity to Joe. We were just the same faces that he had seen come and go for his long generations in the Village. Nothing changed; all the news was lousy; all the people on the street were stupid; all the world was against him. After Joe's visits, I'd give the apartment a great

140

cleaning, washing all the corners, dusting madly. I didn't know what I was erasing. It wasn't Joe, but it was all the feelings one had that were strange and uncomfortable. At one point you wanted to be nice to Joe; you suspected that he might have something to say, and yet you doubted it. You wondered if Joe reflected some part of the world that had about it only sourness, a terrible tyranny of misery.

"Man doesn't live by bread alone," said Max, repeating himself, "but Joe does. I swear he doesn't eat anything else."

"I wonder if his book will be any good," I said.

Years later, Joseph Mitchell published a book saying that Joe's book never, in effect, existed; that the manuscript he was supposed to be working on was probably a figment of his imagination. Maybe so. On the other hand, perhaps his book was the first true happening, a new form of art, just as Joyce incorporated in *Finnegans Wake* the fact that some might knock at the door and the knock would appear in those voluminous pages. Joe went him one step better. His "Oral History" was true oral history, spoken out in all those strange mutters and curses as he walked the streets of New York. He did not even need paper. He neither needed nor wanted himself or his neighbors—just a few muttered words and occasionally, very occasionally, the hunt for bread.

la bella francesca

"My mother doesn't understand me."

Francesca stood at the door and repeated the comment once or twice.

"Oh, come on in," said Gogo. "You're such a child, Francesca."

And indeed she was a child. To our aged eyes, she appeared very young and naive. She had just turned fifteen and she was a daughter of our friend Teresa.

Even in those days, teen-agers were trying to come to the Village from other places. But unlike today, when some parents abdicate all responsibility and allow a subculture of the teen-ager to emerge, an area for them to live and die in, the Village when we first went there attracted and yet still sent

144

them home. We knew that Francesca had simply paid the Village a visit, and by evening we must get her on her way home to Far Rockaway. Max used to say, "In everyone young in heart there is a Villager struggling to get out."

"I'm not going back to school," muttered Francesca. "I'm not going home again. My mother doesn't understand me."

"Maybe she would if you washed your hair," said Gogo.

"What's the matter with my hair?" said Francesca.

"It's filthy, that's what. Why don't you go in and wash it, and then we'll go up and see Mary Anne's studio. You can come if you like, but first you have to call your mother."

"I don't have to wash my hair," said Francesca. "You girls are closer to my age than my mother is, and if you're going to act like my mother, I'll go home."

"Call your mother," said Gogo impatiently. "Tell her you're going over to the studio and we'll send you home early."

"Do I have to take a bath too?" Francesca asked.

"Yes," said Gogo, "all over, Francesca. Don't forget."

Francesca came out of the tub, all fifteen years and a hundred and twenty pounds of her, wrapped in an elaborate towel and smelling, I thought, sweetly of youth and lavender. It was not a typical smell of Francesca, and she turned to me and said:

"Italian girls make very good models."

"Oh, come on, Francesca," I said. "Don't tell me you're thinking of running away from home and being a model."

145

"A painter's model," said Francesca. "I know I don't have the figure for high fashion, but I'd be a great inspiration for the right kind of painter."

"I bet you would," I said. "But you have to stay clean."

"I don't know why," Francesca said, "your friends have the dirtiest studios I've ever seen. They wouldn't know whether I was clean or dirty. I bet if I were to find myself a really good painter, he wouldn't care whether I washed my hair or not."

"I bet he would," said Gogo. "They like to pick up the highlights in hair, you know."

"Turn off the lights in the bathroom," I said. "We're wasting too much electricity. Come on, Francesca, let's get moving."

She put on some black silk stockings and then, from her cavernous handbag—she had purchased it with baby-sitting money—she took out a toy stuffed animal, a little tiger.

"What are you doing with that?" I asked.

"I've been reading some French stories," she said. "You know, that one about the brother and sister who walked the streets of Paris with a cheetah on a leash. It makes me feel, I don't know, kind of exotic."

She put it on her shoulder and balanced it there. "Besides. I think it goes with the black stockings."

"It goes better," said Gogo, "with a nipple and bottle. You look idiotic."

"You're getting too old, Gogo," Francesca told her. "Sometimes I think you're getting older than my mother. She's still got good ideas."

As we walked down the stairs, the toy tiger fell from her shoulder, but Francesca picked it up and dusted it off. I saw her hug it for a minute or two, and then she put it back on her shoulder. Nobody, of course, paid any attention to us on the street. They rarely ever did. If a fifteen-year-old girl in black stockings, even when black stockings were rare on the streets of New York, wanted to appear with a baby tiger on her shoulder, it did not matter. Gogo said it wouldn't have even mattered if it was a real tiger, unless it turned around and bit somebody's dog.

"I don't know whether I should marry a painter," said Francesca, "or perhaps just be his mistress. What do you think?"

"If you don't quit talking like that right now," I said, "I'll shove you down in the subway, Francesca, or call your mother and tell her to come and get you."

"I told my mother you'd watch over me for the afternoon and take me around to all the bookshops. She said if we go to enough bookshops, I'll maybe get a lot smarter."

"Well, we've taken you around to quite a few things," I said, "and I'm not so sure you're smarter. Or maybe you are. Maybe you're too smart for us."

"I'd much rather go to see artists than go to bookshops," said Francesca. "Bookshops are dirty. You're always complaining that I haven't taken a bath, but bookshops are really dirty.

Besides, I don't like the smell of books and I love the smell of paint."

We made our way down Sixth Avenue and turned east on Fourteenth Street.

"I wasn't made for Far Rockaway," Francesca complained. "I mean, some people are made for a place and some aren't. I certainly wasn't made for Far Rockaway."

"I don't imagine very many people were," I said, "but they've got great clams over there."

"You've got no poetry in you," Francesca retorted. "How can anybody get excited about a clam? I'm trying to tell you something, communicate with you; I'm trying to tell you I'm not happy in Far Rockaway, and all you do is talk about the clams. I wish I had a dress like that," and she pointed at a heavily sequined dress in one of the Fourteenth Street stores.

"You'd look like a walking candelabra," Gogo told her.

"You're jealous," said Francesca. "I've still got my youth."

She was right. On Fourteenth Street, not really a Village street, somebody would turn around and look at her, not because of the toy tiger on her shoulder, but because there was something young and vulnerable and very beautiful in her face. There was a collection of art studios over Janice's Dress Shop. It seemed to be the most inappropriate of all spots for studios—downstairs rank commercialism, but upstairs studios overlooking Union Square.

When we arrived at her studio, Mary Anne told us she was

planning to have a show. She explained that it wasn't so much the money that one had to gather together for a show, even to have the invitations printed, but it was the money one had to get together to have the celebration at a Chinese restaurant afterwards. That was traditional. She had asked us to come over, because she thought we had such excellent ideas about how to make money.

Francesca laughed at that. "That's really funny. These two don't know how to make money at all."

"Do you?" said Mary Anne.

"Well, I could model."

"They don't let you model if you're only fifteen," said Mary Anne. "Forget it."

"I look old for my age," Francesca insisted.

"Maybe she could at that," said Mary Anne.

"Stop it," I said, "her family feels we're a good influence on her."

"Nobody could influence Francesca one way or another. You know that," said Mary Anne.

"I don't see why you have to have a Chinese dinner after the show, anyway," said Francesca.

"It's a custom," Mary Anne told her. "Nobody thinks you had a good show unless you have a good Chinese dinner."

"You're crazy," said Francesca. "My mother would come and cook an Italian dinner for free."

"That's an idea," I said. "You can't live on Fourteenth Street and be such a conformist, Mary Anne. Let Teresa come over and cook the dinner."

"They'll think I'm a flop if I have a spaghetti dinner instead of going out to a Chinese restaurant." Mary Anne looked very wistful.

"We're all flops with chopsticks, anyway," said Gogo. "We're all trying to be some kind of Orientalists. We're just making Chinese restaurants wealthy."

"Come on, Mary Anne, change your tune. I think it's a good idea. We could have an Italian dinner just as well."

"They all like Chinese food," insisted Mary Anne. "You know, Kuniyoshi and the Soyers—everyone likes Chinese food."

"Then use your head," said Francesca. "Let Agatha print the menus."

"What menus?"

"Let's go down to the Chinese restaurants," said Francesca, "and find out if we can't print some menus for them. Then maybe they'd give us a free dinner."

"That's not a bad idea," I said. "We'll get Manuel to go along with us."

"I'll come too," said Francesca.

"I think you'd better go home," I said. "Your mother'll want you for dinner."

"When I called her up I told her I was staying with you for dinner."

"Oh, come on then," I said. "I'll call Manuel and have him meet us along the way."

It was a pleasant late afternoon, and all of us started the long walk down Broadway to Chinatown.

"You've got to admit I get good ideas." Francesca smiled.

By the time we reached Chinatown, I could see she was playing some role—the Dragon Lady probably. The first few restaurants that we went to were pretty discouraging. They were not impressed by Manuel, and all the owners of the restaurants suddenly lapsed into a Mandarin dialect. English was far beyond their capabilities. But Gogo always knew people, and Gogo knew Shavey Lee, who was then the Mayor of Chinatown. We collected enough orders to keep Agatha busy, and Mary Anne and her friends were to be well fed. Whatever success Mary Anne had in the papers wouldn't matter; the real success was in the elaborate dinner that everyone would have afterwards in Chinatown.

As we moved around from restaurant to restaurant, we got fussier as to where the banquet should be. We finally decided on a progressive one—shrimp toast and fried wonton at one spot, winter-melon soup at another, shredded pork at another.

"This is great," Francesca said. "I could come over here and go to college and put myself through school just collecting menu printing for you girls."

"I get sick of Chinese food," I said.

"It was a great idea, all the same. And next week," she said, "we'll go to the Hungarian section. Then we can have a big Hungarian party. After that, we can go up to Eighty-sixth Street in time for the beer festival."

"You're an entrepreneur," I said.

"At heart, I'm an artist's model," she said pertly.

A little later, as we started her on the way home, she said good night and then added, "Don't worry, girls, even you were young once."

the secrets of bleecker street

Bleecker Street is a sea of life; it has many moods. It courses through the Village as might the Gulf Stream, carrying within its wave exotic fruits from faraway places, cheeses, pasta, debris, churches, nightclubs, schools, children, grandmothers, new bohemians, and old settlers. East of the Avenue of the Americas (or Sixth Avenue, as we still call it), it contains sudden hives of patisseries, craft shops that are here today and gone tomorrow, coffee cafés that greet the morning with bleary-eyed windows and bearded waiters sweeping up the butts of last night.

Bleecker Street has always been one of the famous streets of the Village—once it was a *grande dame* that rivaled the dowager-come-lately Fifth Avenue. Now it has only that strange patience of a street that has seen everything. On the farthest west end, moving toward Fourteenth Street, the past is now embellished with rococo antique shops that contain Tiffany glass, oak iceboxes that have been turned into bars, jet beads, old shop signs, cabinets, chests, whaling whistles, George IV pewter cups—the windows cry the wares of yesteryear to small children clutching pizzas, tourists clutching their dignity, and designers who seem determined to return us to the days of solid oak.

When we lived on Bleecker Street, sheltered behind one glass window was Ann Ford's shop, The Little Match Doll. There every Village child, and every Villager still a child, stood in the sanctuary of the doorway and discovered yesterday's childhood. In poses of glorious abandon, in a shop that was rarely open, were wax dolls, jointed dolls, dolls from faraway English nurseries, dolls that had nannies when Mary Poppins was a girl. There was an occasional offering with a price tag—a brass bedstead for a two-year-old, a wicker stroller from some Edwardian Eden—but most of the dolls and toys had no signs, only histories. They stood there in the windows waiting for yesterday's children to reclaim the past; they had that tragic poignancy of toys left in a room by a mother who could not give up her children. Neither wars, nor time, nor the bustle of Bleecker Street disturbed the curious somnolence of a wax doll.

At Seventh Avenue and Bleecker Street, all changes. On the west side of Seventh, Bleecker Street runs horizontal, or as nearly horizontal, as the respectable past. Now it takes off in glorious Neapolitan abandon. Once across the speeding high-way of Seventh, until the anonymity of Sixth, it pulses with life, with color; it inundates the senses with the odors of just-baked bread, newly opened cheeses, freshly ground coffee, and makes it obvious that as Washington Square is, or was, the heart of the Village, Bleecker Street is the major artery to gas-tronomic pleasure.

Italy had many regional dishes; here in the Village everyone evolved his own regional cuisine from the joys of Bleecker Street. Tuscany, with its divergent foods, they used to say in Italy, was the meeting ground of north and south Italy. Bleecker Street is the meeting ground of bohemians and bour-geoisie, Madison Avenue on its way home, the East Village on a shopping spree, the Brooklyn wife sent for the spices her husband—born in the Village—insists upon. This is the street where talk of pasta and passion enlivens every conversation. The Neapolitans have a famous story that a great cardinal once visited Naples. The larder of his host was sketchy, but dough was there and, of course, tomatoes. Dough and tomatoes went together like folk and lore, and they say the cardinal looked with pleasure at the dish set before him.

"*Ma cari! Ma caroni!* My dears! My big dears!" he cried, and so macaroni was named. The story is as dusty as an old pasta shop, but you can still hear it on Bleecker Street. And you can hear, too, a contemporary exclamation as some of the winter's fruit is handled and caressed by prospective purchas-ers. An old gentleman will fondle a pear with the sensuality of a youth. *"Ma cari!"* he'll cry, and walk down Bleecker Street with his purchase, as delighted as John Keats was by the sudden beatitude of fresh fruit juice.

Spring comes earlier to Bleecker Street than it does to even more rural sections. The dandelions are the first sign. The Village world is not a country world, so dandelions do not shoot up from the dormant grass waiting to be captured by small boys, who will decapitate them as they bloom, and small girls, who will blow upon them as they fade. No, the dandelion here is of a more serious nature. It is not meant to bloom at all. Quite the contrary. If it does bloom, it will not serve its purpose well on Bleecker Street; it goes to Bleecker Street only as the earliest, the youngest, the tenderest, the sweetest of all dandelion leaves. By mid-March the dandelions are out in baskets in the streets or hidden in some of the cold little caverns of mystery that serve as vegetable stalls in the winter.

It is strange to see the first sign of spring because frequently in March, since it is so unpredictable, the dandelions will be in one basket and next to them will be Swiss chard covered with snow. Of all the vegetables of Bleecker Street, only the chard is left out all winter long to freeze and grow crisper and more interesting as winter impresses its snow upon it. Children will break off a leaf rapidly, shake the snow from it, and dash away with that curious light-fingeredness and light-headedness of the under-ten-year-olds. But now, snow on the Swiss chard or not, we know it is spring. There are the dandelions, and other signs besides.

157

As mid-March approaches, the bakery shops seem filled with new excitement, and are more crowded with waiting buyers. Bleecker Street reminds every passerby that a festive time is upon us. Ordinarily we are courted by more everyday pastries—*cannoli,* those tubes of pastry filled with Sicilian cream; the *torrone,* always available but generally indulged in at Christmas, which seems a more appropriate time to crack that festive brick of almonds, honey, and nuts; *panettone* from Milan; *zuppa inglese* from Rome; *pan di spagna* (sponge cake) from all of Italy; or such cookies as *biscottialle pignoli* or *alleanaci* (with pine nuts or anise). All of these are the day-to-day bounty of Bleecker Street, but only in the spring do we get the pink and white pastries called *zeppoli di San Giuseppe* to celebrate the Feast of St. Joseph. In years gone by, every Italian home in the Village baked the traditional St. Joseph pastry. Now it is no longer true. Bleecker Street is more content to shop and eat than to cook and eat. But that's unfair. The greatest cooks of the Village still shop on Bleecker Street, and only the pastries have now been left to the bakeshops.

It is a child's dessert, just as Bleecker Street is a child's paradise. And it is the child in all of us that makes it so infinitely exciting to go day after day, year after year, prying into doorways, pinching fresh fruit, and choosing the crispest, most exciting, delectable chicory from Jennie's stall. Luigi, on the corner with his fruit cart, has the most glorious grapes, round as the semi-round tower on Our Lady of Pompeii, the church that commands the street and the neighborhood around it. The early morning is good for Bleecker Street once the children have gone to Our Lady of Pompeii school and before they spill out in all their exuberance for lunch.

Years ago we had many pushcarts. The few that are left are properly licensed, and only a few diehards continue to man them. From time to time there is a great clamor in the Village as a rumor spreads that the Department of Markets has decided to discontinue the use of carts completely. And a wail and a cry that can be heard all the way to Italy is elicited, not necessarily from the owners of the carts but from those true owners of Bleecker Street, the buyers. When I was a girl on Bleecker Street years ago, there used to be two prices—English and Italian in most of the stalls—and it was wise to acquire what I called a "Bleecker Street Italian," which consisted of the prices for chicory and escarole, for artichokes, for the basil leaves that will come in the summer. But now it is still spring. The Feast of St. Joseph, celebrated in the high glory of *zeppoli,* barely passes when an even more remarkable festivity occurs. It is the season of the snail!

Most of the shellfish on Bleecker Street is evident to the eye. It is in Bleecker Street's prime marketing device—a bushel basket out on the sidewalk for all to see. The snails seem frisky, perhaps larger than last year. They are not, of course, the real product of Bleecker Street at all. In fact, quite a few things on Bleecker Street come from a great distance—the dry cod comes from as far away as Spain; the prosciutto from Italy, along with all the cheeses, the imported pasta, and some of those great jars with the colorful pimientos, olives, dried mushrooms. But more exotic than all, the snail comes from North Africa—from Morocco. Here on Bleecker Street the shells look as inviting as they might in the Casbah—and Bleecker Street itself, dark now on a March morning, crowds soon with people and becomes our own Village Casbah, infinitely mysterious, exciting. And here in the fish store we find the Moroccan snail ready to be gathered up, embraced, extolled, almost deified by the cooks of the Village.

But the symphony of bread never changes on Bleecker Street; most of the famous "Italian bread" served throughout the city comes from these shops. Bleecker Street has a word for it—*companatico,* that which goes with bread—and in the Village, as they say, anything goes.

Bleecker Street glorifies the summer with fruit and vegetables. I still carry to the country in the summer herbs from Bleecker Street, and the best of the vegetables. No farm stand seems able to rival the crisp arrogance of Bleecker Street fruits and salad greens.

Fall to winter barely changes on Bleecker Street. In the homes, however, the cuisine will change. Try *baccala e ceci*—Bleecker Street dried cod and chick peas—or for a cold night, recapture the memory of summer with a hot dip of anchovies and oil speared by chunks of raw cabbage and cauliflower. The children of the Village have sophisticated palates, and I've seen five-year-olds approach *bagna calda* with reluctance and

160

retire only when it has been thoroughly licked from every finger.

Bleecker Street is for children at Christmas. The Nativity scene of Our Lady of Pompeii looks down on a forest of Christmas trees, and because of the bounty of Bleecker Street, the heritage of the Mediterranean sun warms the spirit as distinctly as the hot chestnuts from the vendor at the corner warm the hand. *Buon Natale* say the streamers in the shops— *Buon Natale,* and because it is Bleecker Street, *buon appetito.*

pails of snails

Living on Bleecker Street meant that I wanted to try the more exotic foods. So naturally I had to try a feast of snails, but first I had to convince Gogo.

"Come on, Gogo," I said, "snails are good, and they're easy enough to cook."

"Ugh," she said.

"What do you mean, ugh? Snails are great. How do you ever expect to be a bohemian without eating a snail?"

"I don't have to eat snails," she said, "or chocolate-covered cockroaches, or any other of your weird discoveries. Double ugh."

"Well, you don't have to eat them." I gave in grudgingly. "All you have to do is help me cook them. They're easy."

"They're slimy," she said. "Don't forget when we were kids

you tried to get me to eat worms. Oh, yes you did. I distinctly remember your making me a worm sandwich."

"That wasn't a worm sandwich; that was a mud pie. In Africa they eat a lot of mud. It's good for the digestion."

"You've got an answer for everything." She sighed deeply.

"Snails are cheap," I said. "We can buy buckets of them and have a party."

"Some of our friends *deserve* snails." Gogo smiled maliciously. "Can't you just see Betty Lou looking into a snail's eye. Or can't you see a snail looking into Betty Lou's eye. I wonder if a snail has a bigger brain than Betty Lou?"

"We'll invite everybody," I said ecstatically, warming up to the idea of a party.

"You're the Ulcer Maxwell of Bleecker Street," said Gogo. "The hostest with the mostest. Not money, of course—just ideas. I suppose you'll print up invitations, 'Come Sup with Snails.' "

"It's a nice idea," I said. "I'll get Mary Anne to decorate the invitations."

"Someday," Gogo said, "you'll be sending out an invitation 'Come Throw up with Toads.' That will be the end."

"You're not adventurous," I scolded. "Come help me buy them."

"What? The toads?"

"No, stupid. The snails."

"I'll go with you—but you can carry them and you can eat them."

When we got to the fish store, we stood hesitantly in front watching the snails jostle each other in the wicker baskets.

"Where's your pail?" Benny, the fishmonger, asked.

"We don't have a pail," I said.

"You'll need a pail. Snails don't like paper bags."

"Is that what they eat," said Gogo, "paper bags? The snails eat paper bags and then my sister, the nut, eats the snails. What kind of a pail do we need? A garbage pail? That's the best place for that delicacy."

"Snails are good," said Benny.

"My sister doesn't think she'll like them," I told him.

"Snails are good," he repeated. "Your sister is stupid. Snails are brain food, and good for the digestion. Wait and see."

Gogo went next door to the paint store and bought two large aluminum buckets. She came back swinging them, I thought rather belligerently.

Benny filled a large scoop, and the snails scattered into the buckets like big marbles. They smelled salty and exotic.

The buckets had no tops, so we carried them very gingerly by their handles. Every so often a particularly peripatetic snail would manage to heave itself over the side and drop sharply on the sidewalk.

"Seon, you're leaving a trail," said Gogo.

A gentleman came up to me and tipped his hat.

"Lady," he said, "you've lost your snails." And he pressed some sorry specimens into my hand.

"Lady," said Gogo, imitating him, "you've lost your marbles, or whatever you keep in that head of yours. When is this snail soiree going to be held?"

"Tomorrow night," I said. "I've invited everybody."

"What have your friends ever done to deserve such a treat?"

"Tonight we clean them," I said.

"Your friends? Oh—the snails! What do you mean, 'we'? There's no such thing as 'we.' Tonight *you* clean them. I'm going to the movies."

We had an old-fashioned deep sink, and we poured the snails into it.

"They look worse here than they did on the street," said Gogo. "I never thought I'd have snails in the sink. Frogs maybe, but not snails."

"At the next party," I said, "we'll have frogs' legs."

Gogo slammed out of the door and went to the movies.

I stood there for a while and looked at the snails. They didn't exactly look at me, but they waited for a moment, or so it seemed, to see who would make the first move. Then they began to crawl.

I had read that snails cleaned themselves. All you had to do was throw in a bag of flour. I climbed up to the top shelf of the cabinet where I kept the flour. The bottom of the bag fell out as I reached for it. I was completely powdered. I brushed myself off, but I refused to be discouraged. I rushed down to the store and bought another bag from Magda at the delicatessen.

"Are you making a pie?" Magda asked by way of conversation.

"I'm cooking snails," I said. "We're going to have a party."

"Good luck," said Magda. "I've got some nice baloney. If they don't work out, I'll send you girls some nice baloney."

"We're having snails!" I snapped at her aggressively.

"Well, good luck," Magda repeated, "but it's really nice baloney."

Imagine, I thought, giving a baloney party when you could have something really exotic.

I powdered the snails carefully with the flour and left a pound or two in the sink for them to eat. The idea was that the snails ate the flour, digested it, and thereby eliminated all foreign matter from their bodies. I left them to their own devices, and decided to join Gogo at the movies.

It was Friday night and the Sheridan Square movie house was filled with friends. I told them the treat they were to expect the next night. Bob was enthusiastic, but then, he would eat anything. I found that out when he took me to a Greek restaurant and ate a lamb's head—including the eye. Mary Anne was ecstatic. She had learned to eat snails in France, but a lot of our other friends, usually eager for a free meal, suddenly had other dates.

"Will there be anything else?" Max wanted to know. "You know, baloney, or something like that."

"I'm going to cook them in tomato sauce," I said, "and we'll have lots of bread."

"Bread and water," said Gogo. "That will make a nice party."

After the movies, we climbed up our romantic stairs, feeling our way through the darkness.

"Shh," said Gogo, "I hear something."

"A burglar," I said.

"What do we have to burgle?" She snorted. "No self-respecting burglar would come near our place."

We fell over each other getting into the kitchen. I pulled on the overhead light.

"Oh, no!" screamed Gogo. "Oh, no!"

There were snails everywhere. They covered the walls, and they had climbed up to the ceiling where they hovered precariously. Then one plummeted down on top of Gogo's head.

"They're in my hair!" Gogo cried. "I'm being devoured by snails."

"Keep calm," I said. "We'll catch them."

"Catch them, nothing," said Gogo. "Let's just lock the door and go sleep in Mary Anne's studio."

"Coward," I retorted. "Who could be afraid of little old snails?"

I took a broom and tried to sweep them up; I took a pitcher of water and tried to wash them down from the walls. Finally, I sat in the middle of the kitchen and cried.

By morning the snails had exhausted themselves. I located them in all corners of the kitchen, trapped them in closets. I put them in a paper bag and threw them in the garbage.

That night we had a party. As Magda said, it was very good baloney. The best on Bleecker Street.

italian harvest

The first Italians to settle in Greenwich Village came, as did Columbus, from Genoa. Perhaps the stone buildings reminded them of their own steep stone cliffs. Perhaps the now tatterdemalion streets reminded them of those crowded streets called *caruggi* in Genoa, dark and almost cavernlike, but sweet with the smell of pastry, with coffee roasting, with the near smell of the sea.

The smell of the sea would sometimes hit you when you least expected it in the Village. It washed in arrogantly from the Hudson, competing favorably, at least until a few years ago, with all the more homelike smells that sneak out of the houses like wayward children—garlic and thyme, basil and tomato, fresh baked bread, sesame seed, coffee, grapes and apples. These are the smells of many Village streets, and wafting over all, just as in Genoa from the time of Columbus, the smell of the sea, the smell of a port.

Guy de Maupassant once spoke about these Genoese streets as "immense labyrinths in stone." But the first Genoese to come to the Village did not by any means inhabit immense shops but rather the small ones that still continue to exist in the Village. The Italians were, however, always great realtors, and they did take over their own labyrinths in stone—many of the tenements of six and seven stories that are today familiar sights in the Village, though some have been converted, and some now tower almost crookedly over the streets. In the nineteenth century, these labyrinths, these tenements, were a center of life—a center of community living that was extraordinary. After the Genoese came peoples from other provinces, until the great movement from southern Italy—the Sicilians, the Neapolitans—who placed their mark so much on the Village that perhaps we think of it primarily as a second home of southern Italy.

When Gogo and I first came to the Village, there were still streets in which the Genoese lived—streets that were homes for the Abruzzi, street corners that were only Sicilian, a house that harbored Tuscan families, an alley that belonged to Umbria. Each street or neighborhood and, we soon discovered, even each house, had its own quality. The Italians who seemed so convivial on the streets were, in fact, as clannish as the old Scottish colony that we knew as children. The clans stuck together. but in the Village provinces continued to stick together even more than, it appeared, the family. The family was beginning to disperse. Members would move to all sections of the city—even outside the city to Long Island or to Queens—but there were still old ladies from Sicily who would not move into a building that contained families from Genoa. There were still girls nearly as young as the two of us who were warned that they could not, of course, marry an Irishman or a Scot, but also they must not marry a fellow from Mantua or Pavia.

We were fortunate in our earliest days in the Village in meeting Maria Nazzaro, and it was Maria who taught us the ways of the Italian section of the Village.

"Look," she would say, grabbing my arm on the corner of Bleecker Street, "that lady is a *strega,* a witch."

Gogo and I would stand there, goggle-eyed. The woman looked pleasant enough. Of course, she wore black, but we were prepared to accept that from all of the ladies of Bleecker Street. But there was little to identify her with a *strega.*

"How do you know?" we asked.

"Everybody knows," said Maria. "One always knows about a witch, but a good way of course is to stand at the church on Christmas Eve. She'll come, but she won't be able to walk inside."

Maria had lived in the Village all her life and knew all the ins and outs of the way of life as well as she knew the streets and the houses. She taught us the feast days and the proper food to prepare. She taught us to make our own spaghetti. For the first time, we learned about *al dente* (to the tooth); that pasta was something that should not slide in embarrassment from a can, but should have dignity and respect. She would take us down Bleecker Street and point out a stand that belonged to a Genoese gentleman who had now become wealthy in real estate, but who still had his cart filled with fish. She had showed how we could identify the fish: the white bait as delicate as minnows, and indeed they were minnows; langustines, or baby lobsters; the octopus; all would be made into a great *fritto misto pesce*. She taught us to buy handfuls and then pots of basil, to make the wonderful *pasta del pesto* from basil of Genoa. And we ran the dried ingredients of minestrone soup through our fingers.

We would walk a block or two and then she would instruct us in the magic of Sicily. You could see that the people crowding the street must be Sicilians, filled as the street was with fruit. The Sicilian and the orange and the lemon are almost inseparable. And the sweets—they loved their pastries, the *cassete* and the *cannoli*.

Once when we were ill, perhaps from too much *cannoli*, Maria suggested an Italian doctor she knew. His office looked almost like one of the shops—a helter-skelter of pills, decanters, and curiously enough, a string of red pepper and a bowlful of garlic.

"Good cures," he'd say, "if you like them."

If she did not recommend a doctor, she recommended a baker. If not a baker, a butcher; if not a butcher, a landlady.

"I know just the house for you girls," she said.

And curiously enough, it was just the house. My sister and I lived there together, then apart as we married. One took it over as the other moved away, until well after our children were born. It became our house and a beautiful one it was too, on St. Luke's Place, one of the most enchanting streets of the Village. Daily we followed the passion for pasta and pageantry that existed on Bleecker Street. Everybody, we decided, was pregnant on Bleecker Street, and in those days a pregnant woman was allowed anything.

"Stop a pregnant woman from eating what she wants," said Maria, "and the baby will be disfigured."

The women of Bleecker Street seemed to be determined that their children would not be disfigured. Actually, we never saw a disfigured child on Bleecker Street, but we did see all the expectant mothers sampling, tasting, enjoying, relishing, as they walked down the street. Later, when I married and was pregnant myself, I felt that wonderful pleasure of being pregnant on Bleecker Street, as though there, more than in any place else in New York, one was a part of a rich, teeming, feminine world where pregnancy was part of the harvest of the earth.

at five in the afternoon

The giants of the arts still walked the Village streets.

I remember walking once with Henry Miller, with the snow crunching underneath our feet. Henry had just returned from what he called his "air-conditioned nightmare," visiting for the first time since his return from Paris all sorts of spots throughout the United States.

The cities had been to him as exotic as those of the Continent, and he rolled out the soft southern names of towns to me. He was intrigued by Hollywood, where Marlene Dietrich was reading his work and where he had met new and fascinating people. New York was still rejecting Henry—his best-known books had yet to be published in the United States—but they could of course be obtained under the counter in many bookshops throughout the city. He seemed, particularly then, shy and lonely, as he said that our footsteps in the snow reminded him vaguely of a movie that had entranced him— *Lost Horizon.*

"Don't be surprised," he told Wayne Harriss, who was with us and with whom I was now publishing books. "I sometimes feel that I might disappear somewhere into Tibet." And truly he did look as though he might, as though he were part monk and should be in a saffron robe walking in a different landscape, but his entire literary output seemed to be carved from the very cement of city streets—Brooklyn, Manhattan, and Paris. His landscape of the southern villages, even his descriptions of Greece, were a thing apart, a land of mythological characters that Henry did not know. But the myth of the city of Manhattan he always knew, and he was to make it for a generation of writers to come after him the place of legend.

Anais Nin was a giant, too, even though she stood minute in her fur coat. She was a genius whom the times had not truly recognized either, nor would they until she carved out her own words on her own printing press. Behind that handsome, yes, beautiful face, her sharp, agile mind was in touch with her environment in a way that eluded even Henry and his friend Lawrence Durrell. Anais was the world of the Continent, one of great sophistication, and the arts were so distinctly part of her whole life that it required no effort for her to capture what was going on in the world outside. Henry sometimes quarreled with her, as you can see now from her published *Diaries,* saying that she spent too much time on her diary, that she did not let the material sift down to other levels of consciousness as he had, down through the levels of the cement of the city into the subterranean caverns of the subway and the sewers of Paris. She had been to Fez, which excited me; she knew North Africa well. There was something about her of the soft leather of Morocco, of women dressed in caftans, with their faces veiled, their thoughts shadowy, their intimacy never to be invaded. She wanted, she said, to touch today, and she anticipated the art of television and of the new world that was opening up.

Wayne and I walked with Kenneth Patchen, the poet, a great woolly bear, down the long confines of Bleecker Street. Yes, Kenneth had a book; he had many books. Yes, we could publish one book. Yes, he knew what the critics would like— not that we cared what the critics thought.

"But I wrote a poem just last night," he said with glee, and skipped along the side of the curb with pleasure. "The critics will love it; they don't love most of my things, but the critics will love this." And with the snow on the ground, he chanted the lines, "The sea is awash with roses. They flow upon the land."

"You see what I mean?" he said, turning around ingenuously. "You see what I mean? The critics will love it."

I liked it too, and told him so.

"But the critics will love it," he said, and grinned. "They don't expect that kind of poetry from me."

We published his book under the title *The Dark Kingdom.*

180

There were the giants of music—Virgil Thompson making his way through the Village streets, having walked from the Hotel Chelsea. A young man called Ned Rorem, handsome and provocative. There was the father of a whole generation of musicians, Edgar Varese—regal, commanding, a giant to look upon, a giant with a massive leonine head of hair, shoulders as wide as a giant's should be.

And the painters: Hans Hofmann, Franz Kline, Willem De Kooning, and William Hayter with his atelier on East Eighth Street, where one went up the creaking stairs into the studio. It was a refuge from the world outside, a world of intense creativity, where someone had the excellent but somewhat painful idea of having poets and painters work upon etchings together. The poet contributed his poem, sometimes scratching it out in the metal itself, and the artist decorated it in an appropriate fashion. Ruthven Todd and Dylan Thomas, both of their heads tousled, were spellbound by this other art, this art of permanence; here no name was writ in water, but writ in metal.

We used to debate who were the better cooks, the painters or the poets. The painters always won. There was color in their dishes, there was the calligraphy of garlic, the pigment of spice, the shape of roast and bread. The poets were not bad. Once Robert Duncan, otherwise a superb cook, made for us, after a tedious amount of work, a huge pot of clam chowder. He said finally with dismay, as he tasted the end result, "It is nearly as good as Campbell's."

181

Before and during the war, the Village had been filled with exiles from France, and it had a European quality that it was to lose again in the years to come. Immediately after the war, it belonged once more to the young, but for a while there, it was the home of the old giants. One time I met that great giant Hemingway.

A war correspondent with whom I worked after the war called me one day.

"I have a treat for you," he said. "Come on over at, say, five this afternoon."

At his apartment, packed with other correspondents, he introduced the giant at his side.

"This is Papa," he said, as a small boy might.

Hemingway seemed to command the room, as he had commanded a careening truck entering Paris, one of the first Americans to do so in the Allied advance. His beard rivaled Joe Gould's. I looked for a moment to see if there was some ketchup on it; there always was on Joe's. But Hemingway was, of course, immaculately clean, like some great, white, Pyrenees dog. He looked as though he should be out on some mountain-top; he seemed crisp and white, almost like some gigantic Santa Claus in uniform, because, of course, he was still in uniform.

"Seon knows quite a lot of crazy Spanish anarchists," said my friend. "You would love them. Let's go down to the Village and she'll introduce us."

Hemingway, I could see, was reluctant; I couldn't imagine

182

him enjoying meeting my Spanish anarchists; certainly he knew enough of his own. Besides, he seemed very content where he was; he didn't need to go anywhere or do anything. It did not appear to me that he wanted to move, least of all to Fourteenth Street. He was happy in the reunion of war correspondents—not the lonely creator but a man very much part of the world. It seemed to me at that point, as the war ended, that the curious loneliness we all had during wartime was being shed and we were becoming once again one of a group, a country, a world. The lights were on in Paris again, and there was a new light in everybody's eye.

The correspondents were all filled with that incredible vivaciousness that comes because you know you have just missed dying, that your friends have just missed dying, that for a while, life may be safe again, though not too safe. You could sense, however, that none of these men really wanted safeness.

It was easy to say later that many of these men and their friends, Hemingway included, might be self-destructive, but war had taught all of them that man's destruction was, alas, almost an inevitable part of life.

The conversation was extremely masculine, and it was about battles fought, jeeps commandeered, friendships made. One of the correspondents, not a burly man but nonetheless a giant among men whose words had wrung our hearts during the war, put both his hands on the table and almost sobbed.

"You know," he said, "it was the happiest time of my life that day we entered Paris."

183

This was a strange world of men together, the camaraderie of small boys. I felt I was interrupting it, and I was anxious to leave them. I excused myself quietly to my host and left.

The correspondents were living the last days of some giant experience and there was a kind of desperation and unhappiness that I could not share, that I did not want. War for women, I realized suddenly, was a thing apart, far different than it was for men, and I felt strangely shaken as I walked beneath the street lights that were going on, once again, all over the world.

*when the moon was
made of green cheese*

For four months we lived on cheese. It had come about simply because we were trying to make money, a process that we followed continuously, without, alas, much luck. Now someone had offered us an opportunity to write promotion copy for various dairy associations and it had finally been limited to cheese.

It had seemed like a glorious idea at first because we would be supplied with all the cheese we wanted. We immediately began to invite all our friends in and they could, with us, select the cheese they most liked. The first week was glorious. The brie arrived packed-in-straw from Wisconsin; the Monterey-jack from the shores of California; Texas longhorn; Wisconsin cheddar; and a superb cheese from Upstate New York called Herkimer County cheddar. For a week we feasted with our friends, sitting semicircle on the floor together with long loaves of French bread, round loaves of Italian bread, bread with sesame, bread with garlic, bread with crispy little pieces of hot meats.

"Now this is the kind of meal to have," Max said. "I've got to hand it to you girls; you're always thinking up something."

We had invited our ubiquitous friend, Betty Lou from Scarsdale, and she told us it had been the most appropriate meal we had offered in a long time.

"The cheese is every bit as good as we have at home," she said grandly.

"Oh," said Gogo, "have you converted the six-car garage into a dairy farm?"

Betty Lou paid her no attention but reached for another piece of bread and a great hunk of Wisconsin cheddar.

Robert Duncan, the poet, was a new figure on the scene and his favorite was to be Montereyjack. He knew what wines, too —what California wines—were the best, and he added an element of chichi that even New York didn't have, coming as he did from what was then thought of as the Paris of the West— that great metropolitan city of San Francisco. Besides his poetry was superb, and we would listen to it, crunching bread and licking our fingers and hearing his sonorous voice, every bit as fine as any living poet, although Robert then was just an eloquent and handsome boy.

Howard, too, was a new face. He appeared irregularly during the war and continued to ship out with the Merchant Marine after the war. He brought things from faraway countries —artifacts from Peru, wedding jewelry from Guatemala, alpaca blankets from Chile.

He lectured us on cheese; the great cheeses of England— Cheshire, Stilton, Lancashire. And he was eloquent about French cheeses; Casanova, he reminded us, had felt that Roquefort was the cheese of love. We soon discovered that often too much Roquefort swiftly meant an upset stomach.

We tried every recipe we knew. I made my very first, very poor Welsh rabbit, and after the Welsh rabbit, we had tomato and cheese puddings; we had cheese flan taught to us by Russian friends. We had cheese omelets and *tortillas con queso* and cheese puddings. For an ordinary day, there was macaroni and cheese. For important days, there was cheese Charlotte. For breakfast there were baked cheese eggs; for luncheon there was onion soup with grated cheese; for dinner there was veal with mozzarella.

"I can't eat another bite," said Gogo, pushing the dish away. "I never want to see cheese again."

"They say," I told her kindly, "that you write better about it, not in fresh new excitement, but when you're tired of the subject."

"I'm more than tired of it," said Gogo, "I'm sick of it; I think I'm going to throw up."

"Don't," I said, "unless you do it on paper. I mean, write it all out on paper and you'll feel better."

So we wrote about cheese. We were ecstatic about it—we compared it to the moon, we wrote about the great lovers who had eaten it. We remembered Heidi and the goat cheese in the mountains. We remembered Wordsworth and his sister walking through the hills, carrying nothing but a hard piece of cheese. We wrote about the Australian outback, where explorers would occasionally find a piece of bushman's cheese. We wrote about cheese and apples, and cheese and meat, and cheese and wine. We wrote about cheese, and got hungrier and hungrier because we could no longer eat cheese and the money had yet to come.

"It will come at the end of the month," said Gogo, "and then I'll have nothing but chicken—that is, chicken without cheese, and bread without cheese, soup without cheese, veal without cheese, vegetables without cheese."

"I'll have steak," I said. "Steak without cheese, tomatoes without cheese, bread without cheese."

Betty Lou came one afternoon while we were fortunately having a cup of tea without cheese, and she said, "Isn't there something around for a wee sandwich?"

"There's not a thing in the house," I said. "Not an absolute thing. We're cleaned out—we have to wait for that check. We'll get by one way or another. Bob is taking me out tonight, Bill's taking Gogo, and then we've got dates for the rest of the

189

week. But in the meantime, the larder is bare. You've come to the original Old Mother Hubbard's."

"I'll send you something," she said in her Lady Bountiful voice.

Of course, she did; a basket of assorted cheeses from Bloomingdale's.

snows on the street

Miss Verity Thompson was a member of the Society of the Great Blizzard.

We met her first one day in Miss Douglas' bakeshop on West Fourth Street. It was a late May day and warm outside, and the aromas of the bakery itself were so enveloping that we were almost too warm and too contented. But not Miss Thompson. She stood, huddled in the corner, in an elaborate fur coat that hit her anklebone, and she appeared to be almost shivering. She carefully ordered what she wanted—one date bar and one perfect blueberry muffin.

Miss Douglas' date bars were famous; so were the blueberry muffins; so were the coconut cakes; so were the devil's-food cakes; so were the chocolate cakes. Each season something more tempting and exciting wafted out of the door with a scent utterly beguiling. At Christmas time, she made ginger-bread men and trees and animals. They hung all over the shop, festive creatures halfway between reality and fantasy—horses that were almost unicorns, gingerbread men that were almost leprechauns, and Christmas trees that were almost some exotic plant. She made cheese cookies that melted in the mouth, pumpkin pie that my uncle would come miles to get, mince-meat that rivaled that of Dickens' London.

She knew everyone, or better still, everyone eventually came to her shop, and if you were a regular patron, you would be able to see some of the Village you would not otherwise be likely to see. You would not, for example, often see Miss Thompson on the street. She would pick up her two purchases, turn up her collar, and disappear. She lived in a house such as the one that belonged to Miss Willis and the parrot, Village Pete—a house that had belonged to her father and his father before him and his father before that.

But Miss Thompson's claim to fame in the Village when we first arrived was not the historical past of her grandparents. It was rather these occasional sights of her, not only in May, but also in June, July, August, wrapped in her great fur coat.

In the winter, we did not see her at all, except on one very snowy day. We were at the drugstore, and the druggist, short of staff, asked if we would drop off some cough drops at Miss Thompson's house. Miss Thompson came to the door in the same fur coat which had grown so familiar.

"My dears," she said, "will you have tea?"

But she looked sick and trembling, and we thought it would be too difficult for her to do anything so complicated. Tea would seem to be an endless proposition for a woman such as Miss Thompson, but then she said:

"I'd be pleased, girls. I'd be pleased."

So we stayed for tea.

Miss Thompson went into her kitchen, barely a closet with a hot plate, and Gogo and I stood around open-mouthed as she tried to prepare tea in the heavy fur coat. The water from the tap soaked her cuffs until she was almost as damp as a terrier. The coat itself had rather a wet spaniel look about it, but she was utter equanimity, and turned to us and said:

"I'm cold, you know. I've always been cold. I've been cold since the great blizzard of 1888."

We took the teacups from her, and she led us into the living room, which was covered with fur rugs and blankets of all kinds. The skins had perhaps been badly prepared or they were too old, but the fur hung down from most of them as though the whole room had been subjected to some great and terrible battle, or as though Jack London's wolves and dogs had come together, fighting mad, and disaster had been the result.

"My father gave me these blankets," said Miss Thompson. "He knew I was cold because of the blizzard of 1888, you know."

Gogo, sensing the old lady's confusion, said sweetly, "I'm always cold too, and sometimes I like to sleep under a rug."

"Oh, my," said Miss Thompson, "isn't that nice. You shall

have one of these fur rugs someday. Perhaps when I'm gone," and her voice trailed off.

I coughed on my tea. It would be just too much if Gogo brought one of those rugs home, because it seemed as I sat there that I could see the fur peel off bit by bit like some great shaggy dog in the midst of his spring molting.

The room was large and cavernous, and it was cold, icy cold.

"Did they charge the cough drops?" she asked.

No mention had been made of money. She was one of the few people that, as we encountered her in the shops in the Village, sweetly said, "Charge it." And "Charge it" was accepted. Charges were rare in the Village. Life was too precarious; people changed addresses too much. But they knew that Miss Thompson would stay in this house, would stay forever, and eventually would pay up from what little money she had.

It became our practice, whenever we ran into Miss Thompson outside of the flower shop, or once hovering near Sutter's, to accompany her home and have another cup of tea. In the dead of winter, we would go perhaps once a month. She would come to her door, the fur coat often covered by another fur coat to protect it. So she was like some great, lumbering Saint Bernard. With her two fur coats, she could barely walk. She had taken stitches out around the sleeves to give herself some movement of her arms, and she wore around her neck some heavy, black jet jewelry when she was confined in her house during the winter. Not so much for decoration, one felt, but rather so that the weight of it might press the fur down and enable her to see over this false bosom of raccoon and seal that she carried around with her.

Her top fur coat was worse than the one under it. If you brushed against her, the fur fell gently to the floor. She was, Gogo used to say later, the only thoroughly mangy Villager, but she was always a thoroughly lovable one.

On one of our winter visits to her house, she took us around to see her rooms, showing a beautiful cherry-wood desk where Washington had once sat and which had a secret compartment. She had Hepplewhite chairs, some Duncan Phyfe chairs, and beautiful china—just odd pieces that had been saved over the years. On the bottom of many of them—for mostly she ate from paper plates—were still pasted-on inscriptions on white slips of paper, telling the time that the dish had been received or the time it had stopped being used on the Thompson table. There were a few framed pictures: one, an old map of Greenwich Village; another an even older map of Brooklyn, where her mother's family had been among the first landowners. She seemed to retain a little of that quaint old Brooklyn speech with which we had been familiar, through our aunt, since childhood. She had a cousin in Brooklyn, her only remaining relative, but they had not seen each other for forty years.

She used to say to us, "Beatrice, you know, cannot cross the water."

"Oh," said Gogo, "can't she even go under the water in the subway?"

"Oh, it's not that," said Miss Thompson. "It's not really crossing the water. I don't mean that she can't take a bridge or can't take a subway. It's just that it's a . . ."

"A block," I said. "Perhaps she just feels that it's another world altogether and she cannot reach it."

"Exactly," said Miss Thompson. "And I feel the same way. I have not been up beyond Fourteenth Street since that day."

"What day was that?" asked Gogo.

"The first day of the great blizzard," said Miss Thompson.

Then she added in sudden memory, "As a child I used to love to go uptown. It was all horses and drays and carts and vans, you know. But even here in the Village, there were traffic jams—as there are today. I used to love to hear the sound of the butcher's cart and the workhorses in the old stable over on Thirteenth Street."

"Even then, of course," said Miss Thompson, "I was always cold. It used to be cold riding in a hack. And the floors of the horsecars were freezing. Even though there would be a stove and I would sit at one with my father, it was impossibly cold. And I remember the straw on the floors when it began to snow that awful day." Her voice went quiet.

We had heard before of people who remembered that great snow, but to none did it seem to have the devastating implications that it had to Miss Thompson.

The Village in the early morning after a snowfall is delightful. The small back yards have a Japanese touch with an etching of snow on the branches and trunks of trees. But within

197

the space of an hour, the snow begins to soil as the furnaces belch out ash and garbage begins to collect.

One whole day the snow remained beautifully white—only because it continued to fall. In a superb gesture, the heavens kept getting it clean again. It would soil momentarily, and then immediately the heavens would open and enough snow would pour down to make it virgin white.

It was barely possible to go out. But we looked at the snow and said to each other:

"We must go and see Miss Thompson."

We fought our way to her street. Some boys had kindly cleaned off a step or two, so we were able to get up on her porch and ring the bell. There was no answer. We rang again. She had no telephone, or we would have tried to call. We stood there on the porch as long as we could, huddled close to each other, and then fought our way home. The next day we tried her again. The snow was piled high, and we could barely make it up the stoop. We rang long and hard. We were rewarded. Miss Thompson finally came to the door. She had added to her fur coats a large fur hat, the kind that the Indians of Peru wear, and she had put on long mittens that fit over, rather than under, the sleeves of the coat, giving her an enormous elephantiasis of the arms.

"My dears," she said, "my dears. I don't know if you should come in. I have no heat. I think something has broken down."

"Do you have food?" I said. "Can you cook?"

She began to weep. "A cup of tea would be nice," she said, "but I can't seem to turn the stove on."

Gogo and I took a quick tour of the house. The stove wouldn't light. We knew what that meant. The gas had been shut off. We tried to flick on some electricity, but that was off too. And probably the poor dear had run out of coal. If we left her there, she would die. If we took her away . . .

"Well," Gogo whispered to me, "take her away and she may die too."

Miss Thompson seemed to have shrunken in her enormous fur coats, and we debated about what to do. Then we went to Riker's, and brought her back some hot food and tea. Gogo, who could put wheels into motion, did so. Somehow or other, from someone, she arranged for coal to be delivered and, in a day, the electricity was on and so was the gas. We did not see Miss Thompson for a couple of weeks, but the next time that we stopped by, she smiled gently and said:

"Girls, you made me the warmest since that terrible day of the great blizzard."

something's happening!

"It is, after all," Gogo said, "easier to make money by photography. A great deal less fattening than writing about cheese and more deeply satisfying."

I could do what I liked. I could write poetry or whatever I wanted, but we weren't going to write any more cheese pieces together. I was agreeable. Besides, I liked Gogo's photography. It took us to the fish markets of Fulton Street, the meat markets of Fourteenth Street, to the fruit markets, and through all the black-and-white photographic poetry of Manhattan. People's faces, fruits, the boats on the rivers, the lines of the old pier, the rotund shape of the old tugboats along Christopher Street—Gogo photographed them all.

And there were the people she met and whom she would photograph just for fun. Carson McCullers' sister, Marguerite

Smith, then assistant editor of *Mademoiselle,* had sent to our apartment a sweet southern boy whose name was Truman Capote. I always said that Gogo made a mistake by photographing him straight up. A year later he was photographed stretched out on a couch, looking not quite as Presbyterian as Gogo had made him appear in our living room, and he who was already a great writer became a public figure as well. She photographed James T. Farrell and Paul Goodman, Calder Willingham, and a host of other friends. In the background we played Mozart or James Joyce reading *Anna Livia Plurabelle.* It seemed that everybody we knew wanted to be photographed, and the living room looked now like some Bedouin tent hung with blankets on all sides, because Gogo felt that the softness of the blankets gave the best possible background for a picture. I was furious about the blankets. Sometimes they would cover the doors, even the door to the bathroom, so that our guests had to fumble and swear to themselves before they could make an entrance to kitchen or bathroom or hallway.

"I don't see why you've got to put them over the doorways," I said. "Why can't you put them on the walls?"

"I like the vague light shining through," she said.

And I moaned as I tried to go through a doorway at night and fell over a chair and broke the vase that stood on the bookcase. Furthermore, I had barely got through the doorway when I felt a sharp pain in my shoulder. Claudia, our new cat, terrified of the noise, had jumped from her perch on top of the highest bookcase and landed in fear on my shoulder.

"It's no way to live," I muttered. "Someday soon I'm going to stop being bohemian, get married, move to the country, and have doorways you can walk through."

"You're just muttering," said Gogo. "You'll always be a bohemian. The only trouble with you is you would rather have ten cats than one cat."

"It's the doorway," I said. "I've got this funny kind of feeling that there should be open doorways. Gogo, really you shouldn't go around hanging blankets all over the doorways."

"You don't have the soul of a poet," she said. "You may be a poet, but you don't have the soul of a poet."

When I got ready to go to work the next morning, I felt scratched and beaten. I was working at the most satisfying job I had ever had, one I would continue to have, and will, I trust, for the rest of my life—at first as an editor and then as a consultant for various publishing houses. I liked the work, even if it did mean that you had to read all your friends' manuscripts in addition to all your work at the office. It was no different, though, from Gogo having to photograph everyone she knew. The next time I complained about the doors being covered with blankets, she reminded me that the chairs were covered with manuscripts—big ones, little ones, some handwritten, some poorly typed and some excellently typed, some even with salt between the pages so that people would be sure that I had read all the way through. There were manuscripts that had notes to the publisher's reader right inside, saying, "Ah, ha, I know you won't go beyond here. All of you readers are frustrated novelists."

After a while, I noticed Gogo was taking endless pictures of a boy named Bill, who had returned from a prison camp in Germany. She photographed him daily, it seemed, and the apartment became cluttered with movie equipment as Bill and Gogo began to record the Village on film.

And after a while, Gogo noticed I was reading less poetry and more books on famous engineers—books that Bob had left at the house.

"Something's happening," said Gogo.

"I know," I said.

"Bill and Bob are both Villagers."

"Of course," I said.

"We could live in the Village and have Village children. The children could really *live!*" Gogo exclaimed. "I wonder how one gets proposed to," she added.

"Let's wait and see," I said. "I'm sure it will be romantic."

i married a villager

"What's in the refrigerator?" asked Bob.

"Oh, stuff," I said.

"What kind of stuff?"

"You know," I said. "There's some chili and there's some curry, and some homemade soup."

"I'll take a look."

"Be careful," I warned. "I've got it a little piled up."

"I can manage," he said. "You just don't know how to line up a refrigerator properly. I'll teach you."

"Okay, but watch out."

"For goodness sakes, Seon, I'm an engineer. I know all about refrigerators."

I was very impressed by Bob. He knew all about refrigerators, voltage regulators, semi-conductors, hard ferrites, soft ferrites, computers, physics, chemistry, and he had even painted a portrait of one of my cats. The portrait wasn't very good, but the cat didn't mind. I was worried though: he did know about refrigerators, but he wasn't on intimate terms with mine.

My kitchen fought me. It waited until I wasn't looking: then the gas disappeared or leaked; the drains gurgled like the sound track of an old horror movie; the bottom fell out of the garbage can; and the refrigerator lost things. The chili hid behind the curry; the curry hid behind the soup; an onion fell into the milk container. And sometimes the cats got the hash and I got the cat food.

I particularly envied my friend Barbara Reid. She knew how nasty and difficult a refrigerator could be. She kept no food in hers at all, but instead stored her novel in layers on the shelves. It was better than a safe, she said—a great protection against fires in old Village apartments. It was a brilliant idea, too, until the refrigerator arrogantly defrosted itself, tossing genius in the drink.

"Oh, no," screamed Bob now from the closet that served as a kitchen.

"Did you get hurt?" I shouted, rushing in.

"Oh, no," he said sweetly, "not at all. Only there isn't any homemade soup in the refrigerator. The homemade soup just spilled over my new suit. Seon, you didn't have that soup placed on any shelf. You had it suspended in the air. Where did you learn that trick? From one of your Indian friends—an Indian rope trick for the kitchen?"

"I'm sorry about your suit, but you have to watch that refrigerator. It's mean."

"What's this?" said Bob, dragging out a bowl.

"That's chili, I think," I said. "I couldn't find it when I looked the last time."

"When was last time?" he asked suspiciously. "If that's chili, it's been left over since the Spanish American War. Look, I'll bet even the cats won't eat it."

"They're not hungry," I said. "They're licking the soup you spilled on the floor."

"The soup I spilled? I didn't spill that soup—that soup lunged at me."

"That's what I said—that refrigerator is mean."

"Nonsense. I've done work for the company that makes this refrigerator. It's the best on the market. What's in this dish?"

"That's the curry, I think."

"How do you know?" he demanded. "I think it's got fur on it! Maybe we could sell it as a relic of the Sepoy Indian Mutiny."

"I've been writing something," I said. "I guess I just haven't looked in the refrigerator for a while."

"You'd be great writing a book on household hints," he said.

"Well, I didn't ask you to go into the refrigerator." I was

nearly weeping. "If you don't like it," I blurted out, "how come you don't live uptown?"

"I'm just as much a Villager as you are."

"What have you got in your refrigerator?" I asked.

"I don't use it for food," he said. "I need the space. I store my microscope there and my binoculars, and the miniature atomic plant that I'm building for my nephew. That way the pieces don't get lost—but I do get hungry. Do you think you could scramble me some eggs? Are these OK—or are they dinosaur eggs?"

"Dinosaur eggs are bigger," I said. "But if there were a dinosaur around, the eggs would end up in my refrigerator."

"You're wacky," he said, "but you're nice. I like you; I even love you. But after we get married, I'll take charge of the refrigerator."

"That's great. I hoped you would."

It wasn't quite the proposal I expected. Bob finished his scrambled eggs appreciatively and said, "Let's go get you an engagement present."

"I'd sort of love one of those long flowing Isadora Duncan scarves that they have on Eighth Street."

"They're too bohemian," said Bob. "Wait until you see what I'm going to get you."

We walked out into the Village late-Saturday sun, feeling at peace with the world and ourselves. The streets had never looked more attractive: the fruit at the Balducci stand was round and ripe and promising; the fall leaves were beautiful at the florists'. All the Village faces that we passed seemed familiar, exciting, responsive.

"Here we are," said Bob. "We just have to go down into the basement."

"Is there a shop in the basement? It looks pretty dark to me."

"No, there's no shop. It's just a cellar."

"What's down there?" I asked suspiciously. It didn't appear to me the type of place you would find the engagement present of your dreams.

"Watch out, don't trip," said Bob. "I'll find the light."

He switched on the light, the small wattage throwing strange shadows over all the paraphernalia of a typical Village cellar—old college trunks and bags, pieces of broken furniture, an abandoned refrigerator.

The refrigerator looked worse than mine, and I feared for a moment that Bob had decided upon it to seal our troth—but no, he made his way farther into the darkness.

He came out from one corner in tribal splendor, wearing an elaborate mask and carrying two beautifully decorated African spears.

"There are a dozen spears here," he said excitedly. "They were left here from one of the early expeditions to the Congo by someone who once lived here. The fellow who owns this house said I could have them. I knew you'd love them."

I did love them. They were beautifully carved. Heck, I

thought, any girl could go out and buy her own Isadora Duncan scarf.

"Do we take them now?" I asked. "How do we get them back to the apartment?"

"Carry them," said Bob simply. "Here, we'll each take half. I'll carry the mask."

"Won't somebody stop us? Don't you think we'll look kind of strange, carrying a dozen African spears down Sixth Avenue?"

"Don't be silly," said Bob authoritatively, "this is the Village. No one will even notice."

The spears were over eight feet tall, and they slipped precariously from our grip from time to time. A passerby would help us gather them up without comment. They were more difficult to manage as we climbed my four flights of stairs; they banged and rattled against the doorways of my neighbors on each floor.

"It's all right," I said sweetly to one old lady. "We're getting married and these are my engagement present."

"Isn't that nice," she said, half-asleep. "Such a nice boy and such a nice present. You can find everything in the Village!"

The next day Bob bought me the scarf.

"today the village isn't
        what it used to be!"
don't believe it

Now, years later, I'm still hearing the old refrain that the Village isn't what it used to be, but at the same time, even now on the streets of the Village, I see us as we were then. We stood just yesterday on the corner of Washington Square where a girl addressed us:

"Lady, can you tell me how to get to MacDougal Street?"

"You're there," I said. "MacDougal starts here at the tip of the Park."

The girl appeared disappointed and more than a little confused. Her long glossy blond hair made her look very young—an almost Alice in Wonderland illustration. And, like Alice, she had a look of bewilderment, as though she were seeing the world through a looking-glass, and the image she saw of herself was not clearly defined. She was not as young as she looked nor as old as she thought. She was a late adolescent, wandering as did Alice into a world she had never made—too old, despite her fairy-tale, golden hair, for the world of childhood; too young for the seething world of today's Village.

"Did you expect it to be different," I said. "MacDougal Street?"

"I don't know," she said, eager to talk. "I don't know what I expected. Something exciting, I think. It's just a street, and it looks kind of dirty. But," she added defensively, "I'm glad I came." And she walked down MacDougal, young and proud and expectant.

My daughter, Shivaun, and I watched her disappear: her hair flowing behind her; her gypsy beads swinging from side to side as she walked with studied determination; her bell-bottom trousers brushing her sandaled feet.

"Her feet hurt," said my daughter. "It's hard to walk all over the Village in sandals. It's even harder in bare feet. Why do they do it?"

"Maybe they're on a kind of pilgrimage," I said. "In other days, young people often went on pilgrimages; old people, too, for that matter, to some holy place."

"The Village is fun," my daughter said, laughing, "but it certainly isn't holy."

I agreed.

"But perhaps where she is walking is somewhat holy. Not down MacDougal, but all the streets; we must go down many streets to make a real pilgrimage."

217

"What do you mean?" Shivaun asked.

"Growing up," I said. "We do walk down many streets. Some of them are right; some of them are wrong. Sometimes we choose the streets because others walked them before us. Even Aunt Gogo and I once stood on this corner and asked the way to MacDougal Street."

"You're kidding, Mother," said Shivaun. "You're old!" But then she added kindly, "Did you wear bell-bottom trousers? You must have looked *awful!*"

No, we hadn't worn bell-bottom trousers, but we did wear dirndls, and they looked pretty awful, too: voluminous, Tyrolean skirts that were the Village costume of our youth. After we washed them, it was the custom to dry and pleat them by tying them around a broom handle. Gogo said I liked them because I always had one whipped around the broom just so I wouldn't have to sweep the apartment, but the truth was we all thought they looked romantic with earrings and sandals, and each Sunday we walked around the Park and down Mac-Dougal Street, our feet chafing from sandal thongs, our ears heavy with earrings.

"Our ears will hang down like those statues from Easter Island," Gogo used to moan as she would buy some great new dangling treasure. "We'll get to look like spaniels; maybe no one will marry us. We'll probably end up housekeeping in the dog pound."

"Your bark is worse than your bite," I said.

"I don't know about that," said Gogo. "Let's go out and bite some tourists. I hate the way they come down here and stare. What are they staring at?"

"Maybe because they think we're more free than they are," I said.

"They ought to keep them caged in those buses. They could put bars on the windows, and we could push in bananas."

"They're just people," I said. "They don't *live*. Come on, let's go for a walk down MacDougal."

We would walk down the street, following the footsteps of those who had walked before us. Here near the corner was a shop once owned by a man called Currier, who joined up with another called Ives and formed the great print-making establishment of Currier & Ives. Together they captured the nineteenth-century spirit of Manhattan. Just beyond was the basement of the famous restaurant, Polly's, that made MacDougal Street famous long before World War I. It was there that the old anarchist and poet, Hippolyte Havel, used to shout at the world, and at the editorial board to whom he submitted his poetry:

"Bourgeois pigs! Voting! Voting on poetry. Poetry is something from the soul. You can't vote on poetry."

Almost immediately next door, a far more respectable lady from Boston sat down at the window, watching the young life of MacDougal Street, and worked on a story about her own young life that went down into history as *Little Women*.

Just as young radicals seek out the Village today, they have throughout all its history. MacDougal, too, was the home of the old Liberal Club—its members were the great demonstrators, and Henrietta Rodman was perhaps the greatest demonstrator of all. She decided to be a nudist, but the cold Village apartments put a damper on her demonstrations. Joe Gould was far more realistic when he used to prance and sing:

In the winter I'm a Buddhist.
In the summer I'm a nudist.

On MacDougal, too, the Provincetown Players sprang into national prominence with the plays of Eugene O'Neill. And on MacDougal, there was once another Tiny Tim, black-haired and pale-faced, selling candy and poetry—two pleasures for the price of one.

When we were girls in the Village, they told us the Village had changed. We should have seen it a year ago, or two years ago, or five years ago: but the history of the Village is filled with stock phrases. There have always been, and there probably always will be young people in the Village—young artists, writers, musicians, politicians, dreamers.

And they are still writing on the walls:

EAST VILLAGE TODAY—
TOMORROW THE WORLD
YOUNG POWER
YOUR HOUR HAS COME

To which someone has replied:

220

SEE YOU WHEN YOU'RE THIRTY
STUPID

No, the Village hasn't changed—nor have the young people. If the Village did not exist, a young world would have to invent it—but youth is filled with inventions. It doesn't need drugs to expand its consciousness nor anarchy to grow up. It doesn't have to deny yesterday or be afraid of tomorrow. It does, however, have to find its own streets wherever they are—Paris, London, Mexico City, San Francisco, Manhattan, or perhaps even in Rutherford, Bellport, Oshkosh, Laramie.

But I'm glad that, as my daughter says, part of me will always be a Villager. Meet us at the corner of MacDougal and the Park.